Holt McDougal
Algebra 1

IDEA Works!®
Modified Worksheets and Tests

HOLT McDOUGAL

HOUGHTON MIFFLIN HARCOURT

COMMON CORE

EDITION

ISBN 978-0-547-71114-0

6 7 8 9 10   2266   20 19 18 17 16 15 14

4500457025   B C D E F G

Contents

Contents

LESSON 1-1

Practice A

Variables and Expressions

Give one way to write each algebraic expression in words. The first one is done for you.

> **algebraic expression:** phrase that contains numbers, operations, and variables

1. $a + 3$

   the sum of *a* and 3

2. $5 - y$

3. $\dfrac{n}{4}$

4. $10 + t$

5. $3s$

6. Clint runs c miles each week. Brenda runs 2 miles more each week than Clint. Write an expression for the number of miles Brenda runs each week. _____

7. Tom pays 5 cents per minute to use his cell phone. Write an expression for the cost in cents of using his cell phone for m minutes. _____

Evaluate each expression for $a = 2$ and $b = 6$.

> **evaluate:** find the value of

8. $a + b$

9. $b - a$

Evaluate each expression for $c = 12$ and $d = 4$.

10. $c \div d$

11. $c + d$

12. $c - d$

13. Tina is 4 years younger than her brother Jeff.

   a. Write an expression for Tina's age when Jeff is j years old.

   b. Find Tina's age when Jeff is 15, 20, and 58 years old.

Holt McDougal Algebra 1

LESSON 1-1

Problem Solving
Variables and Expressions

Write the correct answer.

1. Sharon reads for 45 minutes each day. Write an expression for the number of minutes she reads in *d* days.

   Solution:
   45 min in 1 day
   45 • *d* min in 1 • *d* days
   45*d* min in *d* days

2. The minimum wage in 2003 was $5.15. This was *w* more than the minimum wage in 1996. Write an expression for the minimum wage in 1996.

   (*Hint:* Was the minimum wage more or less in 1996?)

   _____

Use the table below to answer questions 3–5. Select the best answer.

3. North Carolina entered the Union *x* years after Pennsylvania. Which expression shows the year North Carolina entered the Union?

   A 1845 + *x*

   B 1845 − *x*

   C 1787 + *x*

4. The expression *f* − 26 represents the year Alabama entered the Union, where *f* is the year Florida entered. In which year did Alabama enter the Union?

   F 1819

   G 1826

   H 1837

State	Year Entered into Union
Florida	1845
Indiana	1816
Pennsylvania	1787
Texas	1845
West Virginia	1863

5. The number of states that entered the Union in 1889 was half the number of states *s* that entered in 1788. Which expression shows the number of states that entered the Union in 1889?

   A 2*s*

   B *s* ÷ 2

   C *s* + 2

Holt McDougal Algebra 1

LESSON 1-2

Practice A
Solving Equations by Adding or Subtracting

Solve each equation. Add. Check your answers.
The first one is done for you.

1. $m - 2 = 5$

   $\underline{+2 \quad +2}$

   $m = 7$

2. $t - 9 = 14$

3. $p - 6 = -2$

Solve each equation. Subtract. Check your answers.
The first one is done for you.

4. $b + 4 = 4$

   $\underline{-4 \quad -4}$

   $b = 0$

5. $p + 6 = 10$

6. $25 = x + 21$

7. James took two math tests. He scored 18 points higher
   on the second test. He got an 86.
   Write and solve an equation to find the score James got
   on the first test.

   Why is your answer reasonable?

   _____

   _____

8. The 3 P.M. temperature was 29°F. This was 4°F lower
   than expected. Write and solve an equation to find the
   expected temperature. Why is your answer reasonable?

   _____

   _____

Problem Solving

LESSON 1-2

Solving Equations by Adding or Subtracting

Write the correct answer.

1. Michelle withdrew $120 from her bank account. She now has $3345 in her account. Write and solve an equation to find how much money m was in her account before she made the withdrawal.

   Solution:

   money in account – withdrawal = 3345

   $$m - 120 = 3345$$
   $$\underline{+\ 120 \quad +\ 120}$$
   $$m = 3465$$

2. Max used 23 stamps on letters. He now has 184 stamps. Write and solve an equation to find the number of stamps he had.

   number of stamps – stamps used = _____

   $$s - \underline{\quad\quad} = 184$$
   $$+ \underline{\quad\quad} \quad + \underline{\quad\quad}$$
   $$s = \underline{\quad\quad}$$

Use the circle graph below to answer questions 3–6. The circle graph shows the favorite colors for SUVs as percents.

3. What is the percent of silver SUVs in 2000?

   A 14.1%   C 32.8%

   B 23.1%

4. The percent of silver SUVs increased by 7.9% between 1998 and 2000. If x% of SUVs were silver in 1998, which equation represents this relationship?

   F $x + 7.9 = 14.1$ H $7.9 - x = 14.1$

   G $x - 7.9 = 14.1$

5. Solve the equation from problem 4. What is the value of x?

   A 1.8   C 7.1

   B 6.2

6. The sum of the percents of dark red SUVs and white SUVs was 26.3%. What was the percent of dark red SUVs?

   F 2.3%   H 12.2%

   G 3.2%

Percent of SUVs by Color

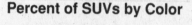
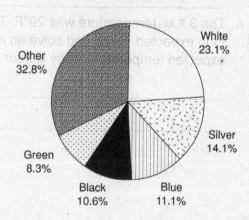

Holt McDougal Algebra 1

LESSON 1-3 **Practice A**

Solving Equations by Multiplying or Dividing

Solve each equation. Multiply. Check your answers.
The first one is done for you.

1. $\dfrac{d}{2} = 9$

   $d = 2 \times 9$

   _____

   $d = 18$

2. $-3 = \dfrac{n}{7}$

   $n = $ _____

3. $\dfrac{t}{-3} = 5$

   $t = $ _____

Solve each equation. Divide. Check your answers.
The first one is done for you.

4. $-50 = 10y$

   $-50 \div 10 = y$

   _____

   $y = -5$

5. $2p = 20$

   $2p \div 2 = 20 \div 2$

6. $3m = 3$

   $3m \div 3 = 3 \div 3$

Answer each of the following.

7. The students at a school fair were divided into 4 equal groups. There were 63 students in each group.

   Write and solve an equation to find the number of students at the fair.

   _____

8. The perimeter of a square is 64 mm.

   Write and solve an equation to determine the length of each side of the square. Remember for a square $P = 4s$.

   _____

Problem Solving

Solving Equations by Multiplying or Dividing

Write the correct answer.

1. John threw a surprise birthday party for his friend. The party cost $480 for a group of 32 people. Write and solve an equation to find the cost c per person.

   Solution:
   number of people × cost = total cost
   $$32 \times c = 480 \quad \text{Divide by 32.}$$
   $$c = 15$$

2. One serving of soybeans contains 10 grams of protein, which is 4 times the amount in one serving of kale. Write and solve an equation to find the amount of protein x in one serving of kale.

   amount of protein × 4 = _____ grams
   $$4x = \text{_____} \ g$$
   $$x = \text{_____} \ g$$

Use the table below to answer questions 3–5. Select the best answer.
The table shows the maximum speed in miles per hour for various animals.

3. The speed of a snail is how many times that of a cat?

   A $\dfrac{1}{1000}$

   B $\dfrac{1}{100}$

   C 1,000

Animal	mi/h
Falcon	200
Zebra	40
Cat (domestic)	30
Black Mamba Snake	20
Snail	0.03

4. A cheetah's speed of 70 miles per hour is how many times faster than a black mamba snake's speed? Which equation shows this relationship?

   F $20 = 70x$

   G $70 = \dfrac{20}{x}$

   H $70 = 20x$

5. How many times faster is a cheetah's speed than a black mamba snake's speed?

   A 0.3 times

   B 3.5 times

   C 10 times

Holt McDougal Algebra 1

Name _____ Date _____ Class _____

Solving Two-Step and Multi-Step Equations

Fill in the blanks to solve each equation.

1. $8 = 5n - 2$

    $\underline{+2} \quad +\underline{\quad}$ **Add.**

    $\underline{\quad} = 5n$ **Divide by 5.**

    $\underline{\quad} = n$

2. $2d + 3 = 11$

    $-\underline{\quad} \quad -\underline{3}$ **Subtract**

    $2d \quad = \underline{\quad}$ **Divide by 2.**

    $d = \underline{\quad}$

3. $3(b + 7) = 30$

    $3b + \underline{\quad} = 30$ **Simplify.**

    $\underline{\quad -21} \quad \underline{-21}$ **Subtract.**

    $3b = \underline{\quad}$ **Divide by 3.**

    $b = \underline{\quad}$

Solve each equation. Check your answers. The first one is done for you.

4. $4t + 13 = 5$

_____
$t = -2$
_____

5. $6.3 = 2x - 4.5$

_____

6. $12 = -r - 11$

_____

7. $-5y + 6 = -9$

_____

8. $-1 = \dfrac{b}{4} - 7$

_____

9. $4(y + 1) = -8$

_____

The sum of the measures of the angles shown is 90°.

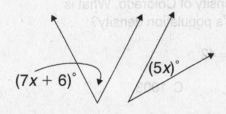

$(7x + 6)°$ $(5x)°$

10. Write an equation for the sum of the angles.

11. Simplify.

12. Subtract.

13. Divide.

14. Write each angle measure.

$\overbrace{\quad}^{A} + \overbrace{\quad}^{B} = 90$

$\underline{\quad} = 90$

$x \underline{\quad} = 90$

$\underline{\quad} = \underline{\quad}$

$\underline{\quad} = \underline{\quad}$

$\angle A = \underline{\quad}, \angle B = \underline{\quad}$

LESSON	**Problem Solving**
1-4	*Solving Two-Step and Multi-Step Equations*

Write the correct answer.

1. Stephen belongs to a movie club. He pays an annual fee of $39.95 and then rents DVDs for $0.99 each. In one year Stephen spent $55.79. Write and solve an equation to find how many DVDs *d* he rented.

   Solution:

   annual fee plus *d* DVDs at 0.99 = 55.79

   $$39.95 + 0.99d = 55.79$$
   $$-39.95 \qquad\qquad -39.95$$
   $$0.99d = 15.84$$
   $$0.99d \div 0.99 = 15.84 \div 0.99$$
   $$d = 16$$

2. In 2003, the population of Zimbabwe was about 12.6 million, which was 1 million more than 4 times the population in 1950. Write and solve an equation to find the population *p* of Zimbabwe in 1950.

   population = 4 times population + 1
   (in 2003)   (in 1950)

   $$12.6 = 4p + 1$$
   $$-1 \qquad\qquad -1$$
   $$11.6 = \_\_\_\_$$
   $$11.6 \div \_\_\_ = 4p \div \_\_\_$$
   $$\_\_\_\_ = p$$

Use the graph below to answer questions 3–5. The graph shows the population density (number of people per square mile) of various states in the 2000 census.

3. One seventeenth of Rhode Island's population density minus 17 equals the population density of Colorado. What is Rhode Island's population density?

   $$\frac{1}{17}r - 17 = 42$$

   A 697   C 1003

   B 714

4. One more than 16 times the population density of New Mexico equals the population density of Texas. To the nearest whole number, what is New Mexico's population density?

   $$16n + 1 = 80$$

   F 5   H 13

   G 8

5. Three times the population density of Missouri minus 26 equals the population density of California. What is Missouri's population density?

   $$3m - 26 = 217$$

   A 64   C 98

   B 81

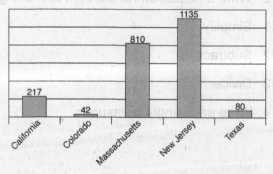

Population Density

LESSON 1-5

Practice A

Solving Equations with Variables on Both Sides

Fill in the blanks to solve each equation.

1. $4a - 3 = 2a + 7$

$\underline{-2a} \quad - \underline{\quad}$ **Subtract.**

$2a - 3 = 7$

$+\underline{\quad} \quad +3$ **Add.**

$2a = \underline{\quad}$ **Divide.**

$a = \underline{\quad}$

2. $-3r + 9 = -4r + 5$

$\underline{\quad +4r} \quad \underline{+4r}$ **Add.**

$r + 9 = 5$

$\underline{-9} \quad - \underline{\quad}$ **Subtract.**

$r = \underline{\quad}$

3. $-2b = -5(b - 6)$

$-2b = \underline{\quad} + \underline{\quad}$ **Simplify.**

$+5b \quad + \underline{\quad}$ **Add.**

$\underline{\quad} = 30$ **Divide.**

$b = \underline{\quad}$

Solve each equation.

Hint: Use the distributive property. $a(b + c) = ab + ac$.

4. $2(c + 3) = c - 13$

$2c + \underline{\quad} = \underline{\quad\quad}$

_____

5. $-2x + 7 = x - 2$

$\underline{\quad +2} = \underline{\quad +2}$

_____

Answer each of the following.

6. Marlo wants to rent a bike. Green Lake Park has an entrance fee of $8 and charges $2 per hour for bike rentals. Oak Park has an entrance fee of $2 and charges $5 per hour for bike rentals. He wants to know when the costs will be equal.

   a. Write an equation. _____

   b. After how many hours would the cost of renting and riding a bike be the same at both parks? _____

   c. What would that cost be? _____

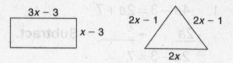

LESSON 1-5 Problem Solving

Solving Equations with Variables on Both Sides

Write the correct answer.

1. Claire bought just enough fencing for either a rectangular or triangular garden whose perimeters are the same. How many feet of fencing did she buy?

Solution:

Perimeter A = Perimeter B

$$2[(3x - 3) + (x - 3)] = (2x - 1) + (2x - 1) + 2x$$

$2(4x - 6) = 6x - 2$ Simplify.

$8x - 12 = 6x - 2$ Subtract 6x. Add 12.

$2x = 10$

$x = 5$

Evaluating for $x = 5$,

$$2[(3x - 3) + (x - 3)] = 2[(15 - 3) + 2] = 2[12 + 2] = 28$$

$$(2x - 1) + (2x - 1) + 2x = (10 - 1) + (10 - 1) + 10 = 9 + 9 + 10 = 28$$

2. Celia is on a 1200 calorie a day diet and will raise that number by 100 calories each day. Ryan is on a 3230 calorie a day diet and will lower that number by 190 each day. They will continue this pattern until both have the same number of calories per day. In how many days will that be?

$$
\begin{array}{rcl}
1200 + 100d & = & 3230 - 190d \\
-1200 & & \underline{\hphantom{-1200}} \\
\hline
100d & = & \underline{\hphantom{XXXX}} - 190d \\
+190d & & +190d \\
\hline
\underline{\hphantom{XXXX}} & = & 2030 \\
d & = & \underline{\hphantom{XXXX}}
\end{array}
$$

Use the table below to answer questions 3–5. Select the best answer. The table shows the membership fees of three different gyms.

3. After how many months will the fees for Workout Now and Community Gym be the same?

   A 2.5   B 15   C 25

4. Sal joined Workout Now for the number of months found in problem 3. How much did he pay?

   F $695   G $875   H $1325

5. After how many months will the fees for Workout Now and Ultra Sports Club be the same?

   A 7   B 10   C 12

Gym	Fees
Workout Now	$200 plus $45 per month
Community Gym	$50 plus $55 per month
Ultra Sports Club	$20 plus $60 per month

Name _____ Date _____ Class_____

Answer each of the following.

1. The formula $K = C + 273$ is used to convert temperatures from degrees Celsius to Kelvin. Solve this formula for C.

$$K \quad = C + 273$$
$$-273 \qquad -273$$

_____

2. The formula $T = \dfrac{1}{f}$ relates the period of a sound wave T to its frequency f. Solve this formula for f.

$$T = \dfrac{1}{f}$$
$$fT = \underline{\hspace{2cm}}$$

_____

Solve each equation for the variable indicated.

3. $x = 5y$ for y

_____

variable
letter for a quantity that can change

4. $\dfrac{v}{w} = 9$ for w

_____

5. $s + 4t = r$ for s

_____

Answer each of the following.

6. The formula $F - E + V = 2$ relates the number of faces F, edges E, and vertices V, in any convex polyhedron.

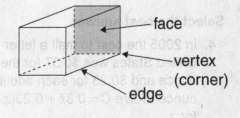

face
vertex (corner)
edge

  a. Solve the formula $F - E + V = 2$ for F.
     Hint: Add E and subtract V.

_____

  b. How many faces does a cube with 8 vertices and 12 edges have?

_____

7. The formula $d = rt$ relates the distance, speed, and time.

  a. Solve the formula $d = rt$ for t. Hint: Divide by r.

_____

  b. How many hours would it take for a car to travel 150 miles at an average rate of 50 miles per hour?

_____

LESSON 1-6 Problem Solving

Solving for a Variable

Use the table below, which shows some track and field gold medal winners, to answer questions 1–3. Round all answers to the nearest tenth.

1. Solve the formula $d = rt$ for r.

    _____

2. Find Johnson's average speed in meters per second.
   M. Johnson ran 400 meters in 43.84 sec. Divide 400 by 43.84 to find how many meters he ran per second.
   $400 \div 43.84 =$

    _____

2000 Summer Olympics		
Gold Medal Winner	**Race**	**Time (s)**
M. Greene, USA	100 m	9.87
K. Kenteris, Greece	200 m	20.09
M. Johnson, USA	400 m	43.84
A. Garcia, Cuba	110 m hurdles	13.00

3. Find Garcia's average speed in meters per second.

   A. Garcia did the 110 meter hurdles in _____ seconds.

   Divide _____ by 13.00 to find how many meters

   he did per second. $110 \div 13.00 =$ _____

Select the best answer.

4. In 2005 the cost to mail a letter in the United States was $0.37 for the first ounce and $0.23 for each additional ounce. Solve $C = 0.37 + 0.23(z - 1)$ for z.

   A $z = \dfrac{C - 0.14}{0.23}$

   B $z = \dfrac{C - 0.14}{0.23} + 1$

   C $z = C - 0.60$

5. Degrees Celsius and degrees Fahrenheit are related by the equation $C = \dfrac{5}{9}(F - 32)$. Solve for F.

   F $F = 9C + 27$

   G $F = \dfrac{5}{9}C + 32$

   H $F = \dfrac{9}{5}C + 32$

LESSON 1-7 Practice A
Solving Absolute-Value Equations

Fill in the blanks to solve each equation.

1. $|x| + 3 = 5$

$$\underline{-3} \quad \underline{-3}$$

$|x| = $ ___

Case 1	Case 2
$x = -2$	$x = \underline{2}$

2. $|x + 4| = 7$

Case 1	Case 2
$x + 4 = $ ___	$x + 4 = $ ___
$- $ ___ $- $ ___	$- $ ___ $- $ ___
$x = $ ___	$x = $ ___

3. $5|x - 1| = 30$

$|x - 1| = $ ___

Case 1	Case 2
$x - 1 = $ ___	$x - 1 = $ ___
$x = $ ___	$x = $ ___

Solve each equation. The first one is done for you.

4. $|x| = 8$

$\underline{\{-8, 8\}}$

5. $|x| = 14$

___

6. $|x| - 7 = 10$

___

7. $|x + 2| = 9$

___

8. $3|x| = 15$

___

9. $4|x + 2| = 20$

___

Troy's car can go 24 miles on one gallon of gasoline. However, his gas mileage can vary from this value by 2 miles per gallon depending on where he drives. The first one is done for you.

10. Write an absolute-value equation that you can use to find the minimum and maximum gas mileage.

$$|x - 24| = 2$$

11. Solve the equation to find the minimum and maximum gas mileage.

___

Holt McDougal Algebra 1

Problem Solving
Solving Absolute-Value Equations

Write the correct answer.

1. A machine manufactures wheels with a diameter of 70 cm. It is acceptable for the diameter of a wheel to be within 0.02 cm of this value. Write and solve an absolute-value equation to find the minimum and maximum acceptable diameters.

Solution:

$|x - 70| = 0.02$

positive:

$x - 70 = 0.02$

$\underline{+70 \qquad + 70}$

$x \qquad = 70.02$ cm

negative:

$x - 70 = -0.02$

$\underline{+70 \qquad + 70}$

$x \qquad = 68.98$ cm

2. A pedestrian bridge is 53 meters long. Due to changes in temperature, the bridge may expand or contract by as much as 21 millimeters. Write and solve an absolute-value equation to find the minimum and maximum lengths of the bridge.

$|x - 53| = 0.021$

positive:

$x - 53 =$ ___

$\underline{+53 \qquad + 53}$

$x \qquad =$ ____m

negative:

$x -$ ___ $= -0.021$

$\underline{+ 53 \qquad + 53}$

$x \qquad =$ ____m

The table shows the recommended daily intake of several minerals for adult women. Use the table for questions 3–5. Select the best answer.

3. Which absolute-value equation gives the minimum and maximum recommended intakes for zinc?

    A $|x - 8| = 32$ C $|x - 16| = 24$

    B $|x - 24| = 16$

5. Jason writes an equation for the minimum and maximum intakes of fluoride. He writes it in the form $|x - b| = c$. What is the value of b?

    A 3   C 6.5

    B 3.5

4. For which mineral are the minimum and maximum recommended intakes given by the absolute-value equation $|x - 31.5| = 13.5$?

    A Fluoride   C Zinc

    B Iron

Mineral	Daily Minimum (mg)	Daily Maximum (mg)
Fluoride	3	10
Iron	18	45
Zinc	8	40

Source:
http://www.supplementquality.com/news/multi_mineral_chart.html

LESSON
1-8

Practice A

Rates, Ratios, and Proportions

1. The ratio of boys to girls in an art class is 3:5. There are 12 boys in the class. How many girls are in the class?

$$\frac{3}{5} = \frac{12}{\square}$$

Find each unit rate.

2. An ostrich can run 174 feet in 3 seconds.

$$\frac{174}{3} = \frac{\square}{1}$$

_____

3. It costs $6.30 to mail a 6-pound package.

$$\frac{6.30}{6} = \frac{\square}{1}$$

_____

Solve each proportion.

4. $\frac{y}{8} = \frac{2}{4}$

   $4y =$ _____ • _____

5. $\frac{1}{3} = \frac{6}{x}$

   $x =$ _____ • _____

6. $\frac{10}{m} = \frac{25}{5}$

   $50 =$ _____ • _____

> **cross products:**
> In proportions, cross products are equal.
> $$\frac{a}{b} \diagdown \frac{c}{d}$$
> $a \cdot d = c \cdot d$

7. The scale of the model to the actual car is 1:10. The length of the model car is 15 inches. How long is the actual car?

$$\frac{1}{10} = \frac{15}{x}$$

_____

8. The map distance between Jacksonville, FL and Tallahassee, FL is about 8 inches. On the map, 1 inch represents 20 miles. About how far apart are the two cities?

$$\frac{1}{20} = \frac{8}{x}$$

_____

Holt McDougal Algebra 1

Problem Solving
Rates, Ratios, and Proportions

Write the correct answer.

1. A bakery bakes 4 dozen rolls every
   18 minutes.

   Solution:
   Find the unit rate to the nearest hundredth.
   Four dozen is 4×12 or 48.
   Divide 48 by 18.
   $48 \div 18 = 2.67$

   _____

2. A boat travels 160 miles in 5 hours.
   What is its speed in miles per minute?

   Five hours is $5 \times$ _____ or _____

   minutes. Divide 160 by _____.

   $160 \div 300 =$ _____ mi/min.

   _____

**Use the table below to answer questions 3–5. Select the best answer.
The table shows the ratio of female to male students at various
institutions in 2002.**

3. If there are 209 women at the US Naval
   Academy, how many men are there?

   A 11

   B 190

   C 3971

4. If there are 7282 male students at the
   Georgia Institute of Technology, how
   many females are there?

   F 2427

   G 2974

   H 8282

Institution	female:male
Massachusetts Institute of Technology	41:59
Tulane University	53:47
US Naval Academy	1:19
Georgia Institute of Technology	29:71
University of Massachusetts at Amherst	51:49
Baylor University	29:21

5. If there are 4959 male students at
   Baylor University, which proportion can
   be used to find the number of female
   students?

   A $\dfrac{21}{4959} = \dfrac{x}{29}$

   B $\dfrac{21}{29} = \dfrac{x}{4959}$

   C $\dfrac{29}{21} = \dfrac{x}{4959}$

Holt McDougal Algebra 1

LESSON 1-9 Practice A

Applications of Proportion

Find the value of x in each diagram.

1. $\triangle ABC \sim \triangle DEF$

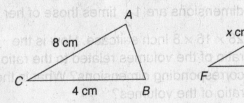

2. $RSTV \sim WXYZ$

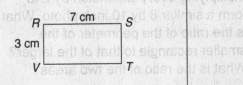
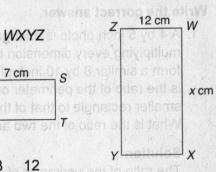

$$\frac{8}{4} = \frac{x}{2}$$

_____

$$\frac{3}{7} = \frac{12}{x}$$

_____

The length and width of rectangle A have been multiplied by 2 to form rectangle B.

6 cm

2 cm A   B

3. What are the new dimensions of rectangle B?   _____

4. What is the ratio of the lengths?   _____

5. Complete the table.

	Rectangle A	Rectangle B
Perimeter		
Area		

6. What is the ratio of the perimeters?   _____

7. What is the ratio of the areas?   _____

Holt McDougal Algebra 1

LESSON 1-9

Problem Solving
Applications of Proportion

Write the correct answer.

1. A 4 by 5 inch photo is enlarged by multiplying every dimension by 2 to form a similar 8 by 10 inch photo. What is the ratio of the perimeter of the smaller rectangle to that of the larger? What is the ratio of the two areas?

   Solution:
   The ratio of the perimeter of the smaller photo to the larger photo is the same as the ratio of the sides which is 1:2. The ratio of the area of the smaller photo to the area of the photo is the square of the ratio of the sides or 1:4.

2. Pamela wants to buy a suitcase whose dimensions are $1\frac{1}{2}$ times those of her $28 \times 16 \times 8$ inch suitcase. How is the ratio of the volumes related to the ratio of corresponding dimensions? What is the ratio of the volumes?

   The ratio of the volume of the smaller suitcase to the volume of the larger suitcase is the _____ of the ratio of the corresponding sides which is _____:3. The volume ratio is

   $(2 \times 2 \times \text{\_\_\_\_}):(\text{_____})$ or

   _____:27.

Complete the table below and use it to answer questions 3–6.
Assume the shadow lengths were measured at the same time of day.

3. The flagpole casts an 8 foot shadow, as shown in the table. At the same time, the oak tree casts a 12 foot shadow. How tall is the oak tree?

   A 24 ft   C 32 ft

   B 30 ft

Object	Length of Shadow (ft)	Height (ft)
Flagpole	8	20
Oak tree	12	
Goal post	18	
Telephone pole		17.5
Fence		6.5

4. How tall is the goal post?

   F 7.2 ft   H 45 ft

   G 38 ft

5. What is the length of the telephone pole's shadow?

   A 5.5 ft   C 25.5 ft

   B 7 ft

6. What is the length of the fence's shadow?

   F 1.5 ft   H 16.25 ft

   G 2.6 ft

     Holt McDougal Algebra 1

Practice A
Precision and Accuracy

Choose the more precise measurement in each pair. The first one is done for you.

1. 3.21 kg; 3215 g   2. 4 ft; 48 in.   3. 3.8 cm; 3.82 cm

  3215 g

4. 5 lb; 81 oz   5. 3 L; 3002 mL   6. 4.2 m; 421 cm

7. 4 qt; 1 gal   8. 2.9 ft; 3 yd   9. 3 c; 25 oz

10. 2 mi; 5285 ft   11. 3.8 m; 3810 mm   12. 6.2 tons; 12,000 lb

**Write the possible range of each measurement to the nearest tenth.
The first one is done for you.**

13. 20 lb ± 2%   14. 30 cm ± 4%   15. 100 ft ± 5.2%

  19.6 lb–20.4 lb

16. 60 m ± 4.5%   17. 80°F ± 6%   18. 18L ± 5%

19. 8 kg ± 10%   20. 20°C ± 8.2%   21. 3.5 mL ± 4%

22. 40 km ± 16%   23. 36 in. ± 5%   24 80.5 mg ± 2%

Holt McDougal Algebra 1

Problem Solving

LESSON 1-10

Precision and Accuracy

Write the correct answer.

1. A bolt in a car must have a length of 37.5 mm ± 4%. Does a bolt that is 39.3 mm long fall within this tolerance? Why or why not?

 Solution: 37.5 · 0.04 = 1.5
 37.5 − 1.5 = 36
 37.5 + 1.5 = 39

 So the bolt does not fall within the given tolerance, because it is too long.

2. The standard diameter of a billiard ball is 2.25 inches, with a tolerance of 0.005 inches. Which balls in the table meet this standard?

Ball	1	2	3	4	5
Diameter (in.)	2.251	2.244	2.239	2.249	2.251

Select the best answer.

3. Ann is measuring the capacity of a 16-oz water bottle. She uses a measuring cup and finds that the water bottle holds 16.2 oz of water. Then, she uses a graduated cylinder and finds that the water bottle holds 16.18 oz of water. Which measurement is more precise? Which tool is more accurate?

 A 16.2 oz; graduated cylinder

 B 16.18 oz; measuring cup

 C 16.18 oz; graduated cylinder

4. Ina added 32.155 milliliters (mL) of acid to 64 mL of water. How much solution does Ina have to the nearest milliliter?

 F 95 mL   H 97 mL

 G 96 mL

5. Jesse mixed 8.24 oz of paprika with 12.23 oz of pepper. How much of the spice combination does Jesse have, to the nearest tenth of an ounce?

 A 20.0 oz   C 21.0 oz

 B 20.5 oz

6. An aquarium must be heated to 30°C ± 1.5%. What is the acceptable temperature range for this aquarium?

 F 25.5 °C – 34.5 °C

 G 28.5 °C – 31.5 °C

 H 29.55 °C – 30.45 °C

Holt McDougal Algebra 1

| CHAPTER 1 | **Equations** |

Section A Quiz

Choose the best answer.

1. Which expression shows 3 less than x?

   A $3 - x$ C $x - 3$

   B $3x$

2. Solve $5 + h = -6$.

   F -11 H 1

   G -1

3. Solve $-\frac{7}{8} = m - \frac{3}{8}$.

   A $-\frac{5}{4}$ C $\frac{1}{2}$

   B $-\frac{1}{2}$

4. Solve $-12 = \frac{w}{-4}$.

   F -48 H 48

   G 3

5. Solve $-3y = -12$.

   A -15 C 4

   B -9

6. Solve $-\frac{4}{5}x = -2$.

   F $-\frac{5}{2}$ H $\frac{5}{2}$

   G $\frac{8}{5}$

7. Solve $0.4x - 0.2 = 1$.

   A 2 C 0.3

   B 3

8. A bike rental costs $4.00 for a rental fee plus $2.00 per hour. Selena paid $12.00 to rent a bike. How long did she rent the bike for?

   F 2 h   H 6 h

   G 4 h

9. Solve $3x - 7 = 5x + 3$.

   A -5 C $-\frac{1}{2}$

   B -2

10. Solve $7b + 3 - 4b = 3 - 3(b + 4)$.

    F no solution

    G -2

    H $\frac{2}{3}$

11. Which of the following equations has NO solution?

    A $a + 2 = a + 2$ C $a + 2 = a - 2$

    B $a = -a + 2$

12. Cable company A charges $75 for installation plus $20 per month. Cable company B offers free installation but charges $35 per month. After how many months would the total cost from both companies be the same?

    F 2 H 7

    G 5

13. Solve $P = 2(l + w)$ for l.

    A $l = \frac{P}{2} + w$ C $l = \frac{P - w}{2}$

    B $l = \frac{P}{2} - w$

14. Solve $a = \frac{b - 4}{c}$ for b.

    F $b = \frac{a - 4}{c}$ H $b = ac + 4$

    G $b = \frac{a}{c} + 4$

CHAPTER
1

Equations
Section B Quiz

Select the best answer.

1. The ratio of pounds of apples to pounds of oranges sold at a market was 3:8. Twelve pounds of apples were sold. How many pounds of oranges were sold?

   A 2   C 32

   B 4.5

2. Solve $\dfrac{2}{8} = \dfrac{3}{m+2}$.

   F 10   H 13

   G 11

3. $\triangle ABC \sim \triangle XYZ$. What is the length of $\overline{YZ}$?

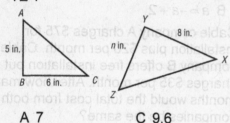

   A 7   C 9.6

   B 9

4. A 14-foot tree casts an 8-foot shadow. At the same time, a nearby flagpole casts a 10-foot shadow. How tall is the flagpole?

   F 11.2 ft   H 17.5 ft

   G 16.0 ft

5. A deer stand casts a shadow 15 feet long at the same time that a 4-foot-tall shrub casts a shadow that is 6 feet long. How tall is the deer stand?

   A. 2.7 ft   C. 15 ft

   B. 10 ft

6. Choose the more precise measurement.

   F. 12 mL   G. 0.05 mL

7. Choose the more precise measurement.

   A. 3 mi   B. 36 in.

Use this table for questions 8 and 9.

Rain Gauge	Rain (in.)
1	3.12
2	2.99
3	3.111

8. Last Saturday it rained 3 inches. The reading from three rain gauges is shown in the table. Which rain gauge is the most precise?

   F. Gauge 1   H. Gauge 3

   G. Gauge 2

9. Last Saturday it rained 3 inches. The reading from three rain gauges is shown in the table. Which rain gauge is the most accurate?

   A. Gauge 1   C. Gauge 3

   B. Gauge 2

Use this table for question 10.

Cup	Diameter (in.)
A	4.90
B	5.00
C	5.03

10. Cups are being manufactured for a set. The diameter of the mouth of the cup must be 5 in. ± 0.04 in. A sample of cups have the diameters shown in the table. Which cup is not within the specified tolerance?

   F. Cup A   H. Cup C

   G. Cup B

CHAPTER 1 Equations
Chapter Test Level A

Choose the best answer.

1. Sarah drives 55 mi/h for h hours. Which expression shows the number of miles that Sarah drove?

  A $55h$

  B $55 + h$

2. Which is a correct verbal expressions for $9 + n$?

  A n more than 9

  B the quotient of 9 and n

  C the product of 9 and n

3. Evaluate $m + n$ for $m = 5$ and $n = 4$.

  A 1   C 20

  B 9

4. Solve $x - 7 = 25$.

  A 18

  B 32

5. Solve $54 = a + 22$.

  A 32

  B 76

6. Which equation represents the relationship "3 more than a number is 7"?

  A $n + 7 = 3$ C $3 - n = 7$

  B $n + 3 = 7$

7. Solve $-8m = 48$.

  A -6 C 40

  B 6

8. Solve $\frac{h}{7} = 6$.

  A -42 C 42

  B 13

9. The product of 9 and n is -27. What is n?

  A -243

  B -3

10. Solve $2(z + 1) = 16$.

  A 4   C 7.5

  B 7

11. Solve $\frac{d}{3} - 9 = -12$.

  A -9 C 6

  B -3

12. If $5x - 15 = 25$, what is the value of $2x$?

  A 8

  B 16

13. Solve $a + 6 = 3a - 8$.

  A -1 C 7

  B 2

14.

Yoga Fun	Yoga for All
$63 start fee	no start fee
$12 per class	$15 per class

  After how many classes will the cost be the same at both places?

  A 5   C 27

  B 21

15. Solve $6(x - 1) = 6x - 1$.

  A no solution

  B all real numbers

16. Solve $V = IR$ for R.

  A $R = \dfrac{V}{I}$

  B $R = \dfrac{I}{V}$

CHAPTER 1

Equations

Chapter Test Level A continued

17. Solve $y + w = x$ for y.

    A $y = w - x$

    B $y = x - w$

18. Nina can braid 48 inches of rope in 1 hour. What is her speed in feet per hour?

    A 0.8 ft/h   C 576 ft/h

    B 4 ft/h

19. Solve $\dfrac{4}{s} = \dfrac{-2}{9}$.

    A −4.5   B −18

20. The ratio of boys to girls in art class is 1:2. There are 12 girls in the class. How many boys are there?

    A 6   B 24

21. The length and width of a 2 cm by 3 cm rectangle are tripled (multiplied by 3) to form a similar rectangle. Which is equal to the ratio of the perimeters?

    A the ratio of the corresponding sides

    B the cube of the ratio of the corresponding sides

22. Kris is 2 meters tall and casts a shadow 4 meters long. At the same time, a tree casts a shadow 10 meters long. How tall is the tree?

    A 5 m

    B 20 m

23. $\triangle ABC \sim \triangle DEF$. Find $\overline{DF}$.

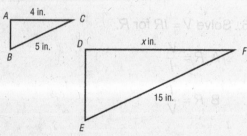

    A $\dfrac{4}{3}$ in.   C 12 in.

    B 8 in.

24. Choose the more precise measurement in the pair.

    A. 6.7 mi   B. 6 mi

Use the table for question 26.

Frame	Length (cm)
1	15.25
2	15.30
3	15.10

25. A frame shop must make frames with a length of 15.25 cm ± 0.1 cm. Three frames have the lengths shown in the table. Which frame is not within the specified tolerance?

    A. Frame 1   C. Frame 3

    B. Frame 2

26. Write the possible range for the measurement 10 g ± 10%. Round to the nearest hundredth if necessary.

    A. 5 g—15 g   C. 9 g—11 g

    B. 9.9 g—10.1 g

Name _____ Date _____ Class_____

Graphing and Writing Inequalities

Match each inequality with its description.
The first one is done for you.

inequality:

statement that two
quantities are **not** equal

1. $a + 2 \le 6$ _____ **a ≤ 4, c** _____   a. all real numbers less than 1

2. $3n < 3$ _____   b. all real numbers greater than 2

3. $f - 2 > 0$ _____   c. all real numbers less than or equal to 4

4. $8 \le \dfrac{1}{2}y$ _____   d. all real numbers greater than or equal to 16

Graph each inequality. The first one is done for you.

5. $t \ge 15$ ← |—|—|—●—|—|—→
13 14 15 16 17 18

6. $h > -12$ ← |—|—|—|—|—|—|—→
−14 −13 −12 −11 −10 −9

7. $b < 3 - 10$ ← |—|—|—|—|—|—|—→
−10 −9 −8 −7 −6 −5

8. $3^2 \ge w$ ← |—|—|—|—|—|—|—→
6 7 8 9 10 11

Match each inequality with its graph by writing the letter on the line.
The first one is done for you.

9. $x \ge -4$ _____ **d** _____

a. ← |—|—|○—|—|—|—|—→
−7 −6 −5 −4 −3 −2 −1 0

10. $x \le -4$ _____

b. ◄—|—|—|—|—|—|—|—→
−7 −6 −5 −4 −3 −2 −1 0

11. $x > -4$ _____

c. ◄—|—|○—|—|—|—|—→
−7 −6 −5 −4 −3 −2 −1 0

12. $x < -4$ _____

d. ← |—|—●—|—|—|—|—►
−7 −6 −5 −4 −3 −2 −1 0

Let h = height. Write an inequality. Graph the solutions.

13. To enter the play area, children must be more than 4 feet tall.

_____

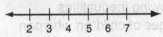

← |—|—|—|—|—|—→
2 3 4 5 6 7

Holt McDougal Algebra 1

LESSON 2-1 Problem Solving

Graphing and Writing Inequalities

Write the correct answer.

1. A citizen must be at least 35 years old in order to run for the Presidency of the United States. Choose a variable and write an inequality for this situation.
   Solution:
   Let a be a person's age.
   $a \geq 35$

2. A certain elevator can hold no more than 2500 pounds. Choose a variable and write an inequality for this situation.

   Let $w =$ _____

   $w \leq$ _____

3. Approximately 30% of the land on Earth is forest. This percent is decreasing. Write and graph an inequality for this situation.

   _____

   _____

   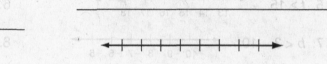

4. Khalil weighed 125 pounds before he gained weight to play football. Write and graph an inequality for this situation.

   _____

   _____

When visitors enter an amusement park, they receive a list of rules. Select the best answer.

5. You must be at least 50 inches tall to ride the roller coaster. Which of the following inequalities fits this situation?

   A $h \leq 50$

   B $h \geq 50$

   C $h > 50$

6. Children less than 12 years old must ride the roller coaster with an adult. Which of the following inequalities shows the ages of children who must ride with an adult?

   F $y \leq 12$

   G $y < 12$

   H $y \geq 12$

7. An area of the park is set aside for children who are 6 years old or younger. Which of the following inequalities represents the ages of children who can go in this area?

   A $a \leq 6$

   B $a < 6$

   C $a \geq 6$

Holt McDougal Algebra 1

LESSON 2-2

Practice A

Solving Inequalities by Adding or Subtracting

Solve each inequality and graph the solution. The first one is done for you.

1. $t - 3 > 5$

$$t > 8$$

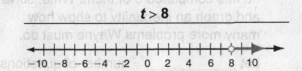

| | inequality: statement that two quantities are **not** equal |

2. $4 \le p - 1$

3. $m + 15 < 6$

4. $-8 \ge w - 11$

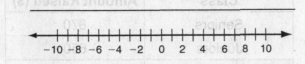

5. $-5 + g > -5$

Answer each question.

6. Joy wants to save at least $40 for her trip. So far, she has $32. She plans to save d more dollars. Write, solve, and graph an inequality to show the values of d that will allow Joy to meet her goal.

7. Roy works more than 30 hours each week. He has worked 17 hours already. Write and solve an inequality that shows the numbers of hours h that Roy has left to work.

Holt McDougal Algebra 1

Name _____ Date _____ Class_____

Problem Solving

Solving Inequalities by Adding or Subtracting

Write the correct answer.

1. Sumiko can watch only 10 hours of television each week. She has watched 4 hours of television already. Write and solve an inequality to show how many more hours of television Sumiko can watch.

   Solution:

   Let h = hours of TV she has left

   $4 + h \leq 10$

   $h \leq 6$

2. Wayne's homework is to solve at least 20 questions from his textbook. So far, he has completed 9 of them. Write, solve, and graph an inequality to show how many more problems Wayne must do.

   Let _____ = number of questions left to answer

   _____ ≥ 20

   _____ $\geq$ _____

The table below shows how much money each class has raised for charity so far. Use this information to answer questions 3–5.

3. The school has a goal of raising at least $3000. Which inequality shows how much more money m the school needs to raise to reach its goal?

   A $m \geq 215$

   B $m < 215$

   C $m \leq 215$

Class	Amount Raised ($)
Seniors	870
Juniors	650
Sophomores	675
First-Years	590

4. The juniors want to raise more money than the seniors. Which expression shows how much more money j the juniors must raise to beat the seniors?

   F $j < 220$

   G $j \geq 220$

   H $j > 220$

5. A business plans to donate no more than half as much as the senior class raises. Which inequality shows how much money b the business will contribute?

   A $\frac{1}{2}(870) \leq b$

   B $870 \leq \frac{1}{2}b$

   C $\frac{1}{2}(870) \geq b$

Holt McDougal Algebra 1

LESSON
2-3

Practice A

Solving One-Step Inequalities by Multiplying or Dividing

Solve each inequality and graph the solutions.
The first one is done for you.

1. $2x \geq 6$

   $x \geq 3$

   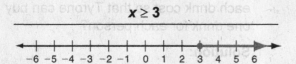

2. $\dfrac{a}{5} < 1$

   _____

   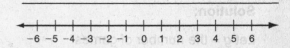

3. $\dfrac{3}{4}b > 3$

   _____

   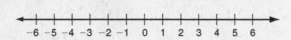

4. $15y \leq -30$

   _____

   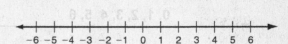

Solve each inequality and graph the solutions.
Remember to switch the inequality sign for negatives.
The first one is done for you.

5. $-3x < 12$

   $x > -4$

   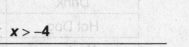
   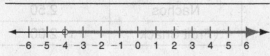

6. $\dfrac{k}{-2} > 1.5$

   _____

   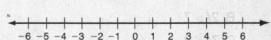

7. $-\dfrac{2}{3}n \geq -4$

   _____

   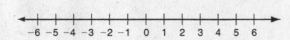

8. $-7x \leq 0$

   _____

   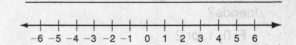

Write and solve an inequality for each problem.

9. Joe goes to the store with $15 to buy salad.
   Bags of salad are on sale for $2 each. What
   are the possible numbers of bags Joe can buy?

   _____

10. Sarah has a store credit for $153. A new CD costs $18.
    What are the possible numbers of new CDs Sarah can buy?

    _____

Holt McDougal Algebra 1

Problem Solving

Solving One-Step Inequalities by Multiplying or Dividing

Write and solve an inequality for each situation.

1. Karin has $3 to spend in the arcade. The game she likes costs 50¢ per play. What are the possible numbers of times that she can play?

   Solution:

   Let g = the number of games

   Games are $0.50 each and she has $3.

   $0.50g \leq 3$

   $g \leq 6$

   _____
   0, 1, 2, 3, 4, 5, 6

2. Tyrone has $21 and wants to buy juice drinks for his soccer team. There are 15 players on his team. How much can each drink cost so that Tyrone can buy one drink for each person?

   Solution:

   Let _____ = cost of drink

   15 _____ ≤ _____

   $d \leq$ _____

The table below shows some items and their prices for sale at the movies. Use this information to answer questions 3–4.

3. Alyssa has $7 and would like to buy fruit snacks for as many of her friends as possible. Which inequality below can be solved to find the number of fruit snacks f she can buy?

   A $2f > 7$

   B $2f > 7$

   C $7f \leq 2$

Item	Price($)
Popcorn	3.50
Drink	3.00
Hot Dog	2.50
Nachos	2.50
Fruit Snack	2.00

4. Reggie has $13 and is going to buy popcorn for his friends. Which answer below shows the possible numbers of popcorns p Reggie can buy for his friends?

   F 0, 1, or 2

   G 0, 1, 2, or 3

   H 0, 1, 2, 3, or 4

Holt McDougal Algebra 1

LESSON 2-4

Practice A

Solving Two-Step and Multi-Step Inequalities

Fill in the blanks to solve each inequality. The first one is done for you.

1. $2x - 5 \leq 7$

    $+5 +5$

    $2x \leq 12$

    $2x \div 2 \leq 12 \div 2$

    $x \leq 6$

2. $-3(k - 1) < 15$

    $-3k + \underline{} < 15$

    $\underline{} - \underline{} \phantom{<} - \underline{}$

    $-3k < \underline{}$

    $\underline{} \div (-3) \div (-3)$

    $k \underline{} \underline{}$

3. $\frac{1}{2}n + \frac{5}{6} > \frac{2}{3}$

    $\underline{}\left(\frac{1}{2}n + \frac{5}{6}\right) > \underline{}\left(\frac{2}{3}\right)$

    $3n + 5 > \underline{}$

    $- \underline{} - \underline{}$

    $3n > \underline{}$

    $\div \underline{} \div \underline{}$

    $\underline{} \underline{} \underline{}$

Solve each inequality and graph the solutions.

4. $5x + 7 \geq 2$

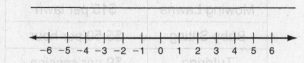

6. $6 - \dfrac{a}{3} < 2$

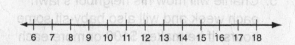

5. $5(z + 6) \leq 40$

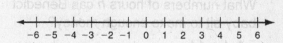

7. $-\dfrac{1}{3}x + 4 > 1$

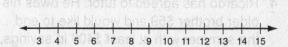

Write and solve an inequality.

8. Ted needs an average of at least 70 on his three history tests. He has already scored 85 and 60 on two tests. What is the least grade Ted must get on his third test?

_____

Holt McDougal Algebra 1

| LESSON 2-4 | # Problem Solving |

Solving Two-Step and Multi-Step Inequalities

Write and solve an inequality for each situation.

1. Jillene scored 24 points in her first game. If she averages over 20 points for two games, she will get a prize. How many points should Jillene score in the second game to get a prize?

   Solution:

   Leg p = number of points in 2nd game

   $$\frac{p + 24}{2} > 20$$

   $$p + 24 > 40$$

   $$p > 16$$

2. Marcus has a job selling cell phones. He is paid $1500 plus 15% of his sales each month. He needs to earn at least $2430. For what amount of sales will Marcus earn $2430?

   Let s = needed sales

   $1500 +$ _____ $s \geq 2430$

   $s \geq$ _____

The table below shows summer jobs and the pay for each. Use this information to answer questions 3–5.

3. Benedict has $91 saved from last year and will baby-sit to earn enough to buy a mountain bike that costs at least $300. What numbers of hours h can Benedict baby-sit to make enough money?

   A $h \geq 14$

   B $h \geq 23$

   C $h \geq 38$

Job	Pay
Mowing Lawns	$15 per lawn
Baby-Sitting	$5.50 per hour
Tutoring	$9 per session

4. Ricardo has agreed to tutor. He owes his older brother $59 and would like to end the summer with at least $400 in savings. How many sessions s can Ricardo tutor to make enough money?

   F $s \geq 31$

   G $s \geq 38$

   H $s \geq 51$

5. Charlie will mow his neighbor's lawn each week and will also baby-sit some hours. If he makes $100 or more each week, his parents will charge him rent. How many hours h should Charlie baby-sit each week so he doesn't pay rent?

   A $h \leq 15$

   B $h \geq 15$

   C $h \leq 21$

Practice A

Solving Inequalities with Variables on Both Sides

Fill in the blanks to solve each inequality. The first one is done for you.

1. $2x \le 3x + 8$

   $\underline{-3x}\ \underline{-3x}$

   $-1x \le 8$

   $-1 \div (-1)\ \ 8 \div (-1)$

   $x \ge 8$

2. $8y > -2(3y - 7)$

   $8y > \underline{\quad} + \underline{\quad}$

   $\underline{\quad} + \underline{\quad} + \underline{\quad}$

   $14y > \underline{\quad}$

   $\div \underline{\quad}\ \ \div \underline{\quad}$

   $y > \underline{\quad}$

3. $3(5n + 6) < 10n - 4$

   $\underline{\quad} + \underline{\quad} < 10n - 4$

   $\underline{-10n} \qquad \underline{-10n}$

   $\underline{\quad} + \underline{\quad} < -4$

   $5n < -22$

   $\div \underline{\quad}\ \ \div \underline{\quad}$

   $\underline{\quad}\ \underline{\quad}\ \underline{\quad}$

Solve each inequality and graph the solutions.

4. $5x \ge 7x + 4$

_____

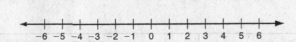

5. $3(b - 5) < -2b$

_____

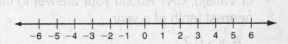

Identify each inequality as an identity (all real numbers are solutions) or contradiction (no solutions).

6. $10 < -2$
   (*Hint:* Is 10 ever less than 2?)

7. $a - 7 \le a$

8. $2(z + 3) > 2z$

_____   _____   _____

Write and solve an inequality.

9. Jay can buy a stereo either online or at a local store. If he buys online, he gets a 15% discount, but has to pay a $12 shipping fee. At the local store, the stereo is full price, but there is no shipping fee. For what prices is it cheaper for Jay to buy the stereo online?

_____

Holt McDougal Algebra 1

Name _____ Date _____ Class _____

Problem Solving

Solving Inequalities With Variables on Both Sides

Write and solve an inequality for each situation.

1. Rosa sells pet rocks at the fair for $5 each. She pays $50 to rent a table and it costs her $2 to package each rock. For what numbers of sales will Rosa make a profit?

   Solution:

   Let r = the number of rocks Rosa sells.

   $5r$ is what she gets for selling r rocks.

   $5r > 50 + 2r$ where 50 is the cost of renting the table and $2r$ is her costs for packing r rocks.

   $5r > 50 + 2r$

   $3r > 50$

   $r > 17$

2. Jamie has a job paying $25,000 and expects to receive a $1000 raise each year. Wei has a job paying $19,000 a year and expects a $1500 raise each year. How many years does Jamie make more money than Wei?

   Let y = number of years

   $25,000 + 1000y > 19,000 +$ _____

   $-500y > -$_____

   $500y <$ _____

   $y <$ _____

The table below shows the population in 2004 and the population change from 2003 of four cities. Use this table to answer questions 3–4.

3. If the trends in this table continue, after how many years y will the population of Manchester, NH, be **more** than the population of Vallejo, CA? Round your answer to the nearest tenth of a year.

   A $y > 0.2$

   B $y > 6.4$

   C $y > 34.6$

4. If the trends in this table continue, for how long x will the population of Carrollton, TX, be **less** than the population of Lakewood, CO? Round your answer to the nearest tenth of a year.

   F $x < 11.7$

   G $x < 14.6$

   H $x < 20.1$

City	Population (2004)	Population Change (from 2003)
Lakewood, CO	141,301	−830
Vallejo, CA	118,349	−1155
Carrollton, TX	117,823	+1170
Manchester, NH	109,310	+261

Holt McDougal Algebra 1

LESSON 2-6 Practice A
Solving Compound Inequalities

Graph each inequality, and then graph the compound inequality.

1. $x > -3$

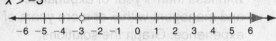

$x \leq 4$

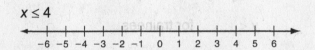

intersection: $x > -3$ AND $x \leq 4$

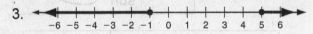

2. $z < 0$

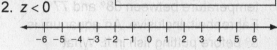

$z > 2$

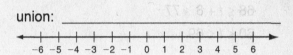

union: _____

Write the compound inequality shown by each graph.

3.

_____

4.

_____

Fill in the blanks to solve each compound inequality. Graph the solutions.

5. $n + 5 < 2$ OR $n + 5 \geq 9$

   $-$ ___ $-$ ___ $-$ ___ $-$ ___

   $n <$ ___   OR $n \geq$ ___

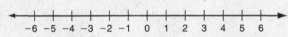

Write a compound inequality for each problem. Graph the solutions.

6. To help reduce pain, Dr. Stoll recommends taking between 400 and 600 mg of ibuprofen, inclusive.

_____

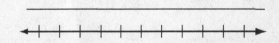

Holt McDougal Algebra 1

ame _____

LESSON 2-6 | Problem Solving
Solving Compound Inequalities

Write and solve an inequality for each situation.

1. A tropical fish requires water temperature between 68° and 77° Fahrenheit, inclusive. An aquarium is 8° before putting fish in it. What temperatures could the water have been before the heating?

   Solution:

   Let t = the original temperature.

   $t + 8$ is the temperature after heating.

   $68 \leq t + 8 \leq 77$

   $60 \leq t \leq 69$

2. A local company is hiring trainees with less than 1 year of experience and managers with 5 or more years of experience. Graph the solutions.

   Let y = years of experience.

   $y < $ _____ for trainees

   $y \geq $ _____ for managers

   $y < 1$ _____ $y \geq 5$

   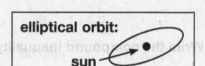

The elliptical orbits of planets bring them closer to and farther from the Sun at different times. The closest and farthest points are given for three planets below. Use this data to answer questions 3–4.

```
elliptical orbit:
            sun
```

3. Which inequality represents the distances (in 10^6 km) d from the sun to Neptune?

   A $d \leq 4545.7$

   B $4444.5 \leq d \leq 4545.7$

   C $d = 4444.5$ OR $d \geq 4545.7$

4. A NASA probe is traveling between Uranus and Neptune. It is currently between their orbits. Which inequality shows the possible distance p from the probe to the Sun?

   F $1542.1 < p < 1703.2$

   G $2741.3 < p < 4545.7$

   H $3003.6 < p < 4444.5$

Planet	Closest (in 10^6 km)	Farthest (in 10^6 km)
Uranus	2741.3	3003.6
Neptune	4444.5	4545.7
Pluto	4435.0	7304.3

```
probe:
space vehicle
```

LESSON 2-7

Practice A
Solving Absolute-Value Inequalities

Fill in the blanks to solve each inequality. The first one is done for you.

1. $|x| + 7 \le 9$

$\underline{\quad -7 \quad} \quad \underline{-7}$

$|x| \le \underline{2}$

$x \ge \underline{-2}$ AND $x \le \underline{2}$

2. $|x - 1| > 3$

$x - 1 < \underline{\quad\quad}$ OR $x - 1 > \underline{\quad\quad}$

$+ \underline{\quad\quad} + \underline{\quad\quad}$ $+ \underline{\quad\quad} + \underline{\quad\quad}$

$x < \underline{\quad\quad}$ OR $x > \underline{\quad\quad}$

Solve each inequality and graph the solutions. The first one is done for you.

3. $|x| + 1 < 5$

<u> $x > -4$ AND $x < 4$ </u>

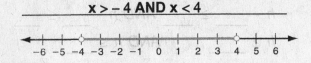

4. $|x + 2| \le 2$

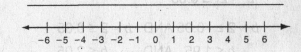

5. $5|x| \le 25$

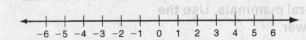

6. $|x| - 4 > -2$

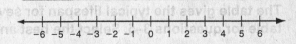

7. In Mr. Garcia's class, a student receives a B if the average of the student's test scores is 85 or if the average of the scores differs from this value by at most 4 points. Write and solve an absolute-value inequality to find the range of scores that results in a B.

_____

_____

Holt McDougal Algebra 1

Problem Solving
Solving Absolute-Value Inequalities

Write the correct answer.

1. A carpenter cuts boards that are 2 meters long. It is acceptable for the length to differ from this value by at most 0.05 meters. Write and solve an absolute-value inequality to find the range of acceptable lengths.

   Solution:

   Let b = actual length of the boards

   The difference between b and the ideal lengths is at most 0.05m.

   $$|b - 2| \leq 0.05$$

   $b - 2 \geq -0.05$ AND $b - 2 \leq 0.05$

   $b \leq 1.95$ AND $b \leq 2.05$

   $1.95 \leq b \leq 2.05$

2. During a workout, Vince tries to keep his heart rate at 134 beats per minute. His actual heart rate varies from this value by as much as 8 beats per minute. Write and solve an absolute-value inequality to find Vince's range of heart rates.

   Let h = Vince's heart rate
   The difference between h and the ideal heart rate is at most 8 beats per minute.

   $$\left|h - \underline{}\right| \leq \underline{}$$

   $h - \underline{} \geq \underline{}$ AND $h - \underline{} \leq \underline{}$

   $h \geq \underline{}$ AND $h \leq \underline{}$

   $\underline{} \leq h \leq \underline{}$

The table gives the typical lifespan for several mammals. Use the table for questions 3–5. Select the best answer.

3. Which absolute-value inequality gives the number of years a goat may live?

   A $|x - 6| \leq 11$ C $|x - 24| \leq 6$

   B $|x - 15| \leq 9$

4. Which mammal has a lifespan that can be represented by the absolute-value inequality $|x - 12.5| \leq 2.5$?

   A Antelope   C Otter

   B Koala

5. The inequality $|x - 17| \leq c$ gives the number of years a panda may live. What is the value of c?

   A 3   C 14

   B 6

Mammal	Lifespan (years)	Mammal	Lifespan (years)
Antelope	10 to 25	Otter	15 to 20
Goat	6 to 24	Panda	14 to 20
Koala	10 to 15	Wolf	13 to 15

Source:
http://www.sandiegozoo.org/animalbytes/a-mammal.html

Holt McDougal Algebra 1

CHAPTER 2 · Inequalities
Section A Quiz

Select the best answer.

1. The solutions for $x + 2 \le 7$ are all real numbers _____.

    A less than or equal to 5

    B greater than or equal to 5

    C less than or equal to 9

2. Which is the graph of $m < 3$?

3. Which inequality is shown by the graph below?

    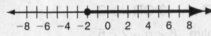

    A $x > -2$ C $x < -2$

    B $x \ge -2$

4. There must be at least 8 students to form a club. Which inequality shows the number of students needed to form a club?

    F $x > 8$ H $x \ge 8$

    G $x \le 8$

5. Solve $m + 4 < -3$.

    A $m < -7$ C $m > -7$

    B $m < 1$

6. Solve $x - 2 \ge 6$.

    F $x \ge 8$ H $x \le 8$

    G $x \ge 4$

7. Sean can spend at most $15.00 on snacks. He has already spent $5.00. Which inequality could be solved to determine how much money Sean has left to spend on snacks?

    A $5 + x < 15$ C $5 + x \le 15$

    B $5 + x > 15$

8. At the express checkout lane no more than 10 items are allowed. Kat has 6 items in her basket now. Which graph shows how many more items she can pick up and still use the express checkout lane?

    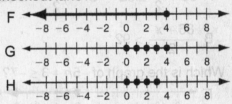

9. Solve $-3x \ge 15$.

    A $x \le -5$ C $x \le 5$

    B $x \ge 5$

10. Solve $\frac{2}{7}x < -4$.

    F $x < -14$ H $x > -14$

    G $x < 14$

CHAPTER 2
Inequalities
Section B Quiz

Select the best answer.

1. What are the solutions of
   $4x + 8 \le -20$?

   A $x \le -7$ C $x \le -3$

   B $x \ge -7$

2. What are the solutions of $\dfrac{2 - 3a}{4} > 5$?

   F $a > -6$ H $a > 6$

   G $a < -6$

3. The average of two tests must be 92 or higher to get an A in class. Bryce got an 86 on the first test. Which inequality represents the score he must receive on his second test to get an A in the class?

   A $86 + \dfrac{x}{2} \ge 92$ C $\dfrac{86 + x}{2} \ge 92$

   B $\dfrac{86 + x}{2} > 92$

4. Which is the graph of $-5h + 3 \le -7$?

5. Solve $m \ge -4m + 15$.

   A $m \le -5$ C $m \ge 3$

   B $m \ge -5$

6. Which of the following inequalities has no solutions?

   F $x + 1 < x + 4$ H $x + 1 \ge x + 1$

   G $x + 4 < x + 1$

7. Solve $4y + 7 - y > 2(y + 3)$.

   A $y > -4$

   B $y > -1$

   C $y < -1$

8. Solve $5(w + 1) > 3(w + 1)$.

   F no solutions

   G $w < -1$

   H $w > -1$

9. Which inequality is shown below?

   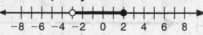

   A $-3 < x \le 2$

   B $-3 \le x < 2$

   C $x < -3$ OR $x \ge 2$

10. Solve $-8 < n - 2 < 5$.

    F $7 < n < -6$

    G $-6 < n < 7$

    H $-10 < n < 3$

11. Which is the graph of
    $6x < -12$ OR $3x \ge 9$?

    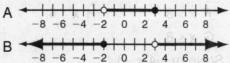

12. Which represents the solution of
    $|3x| - 8 < -2$

    F $x > -2$ OR $x < 2$

    G $x < -2$ OR $x > 2$

    H $x > -2$ AND $x < 2$

Holt McDougal Algebra 1

CHAPTER
2

Inequalities
Chapter Test Form A

Select the best answer.

1. Describe the solutions of $5 < n$ in words.

   A all real numbers greater than 5

   B all real numbers greater than or equal to 5

   C all real numbers less than 5

2. Which graph represents $c \geq 0$?

   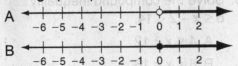

3. Which graph represents $b < 2$?

4. Which inequality is shown by the graph below?

   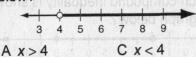

   A $x > 4$　　　　C $x < 4$

   B $x \geq 4$

5. Which inequality represents the situation "the temperature should be at least 40 degrees"?

   A $t > 40$

   B $t \geq 40$

6. Solve $x + 1 > 6$.

   A $x > 5$

   B $x > 7$

7. Solve $m - 8 \leq 14$.

   A $m \leq 6$　　　　C $m \leq 22$

   B $m \geq 6$

8. Which inequality has the solutions shown below?

   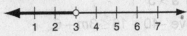

   A $p + 9 < 12$

   B $p - 3 > 0$

9. During a sale, customers receive an extra discount if they spend $200 or more. So far, Erin's purchases total $135. Which inequality can be solved to show how many more dollars d she must spend to receive the extra discount?

   A $135 + d > 200$

   B $135 + d \geq 200$

10. Solve $-2y > 10$.

    A $y < -5$　　　　C $y < 5$

    B $y > -5$

11. Solve $\dfrac{d}{3} \geq 6$.

    A $d \geq 2$

    B $d \geq 18$

LESSON 2 **Inequalities**

Chapter Test Form A continued

12. Mrs. Nelson is buying folding chairs that are on sale for $10. If she has $50, which inequality can be solved to show the number of chairs *c* she can buy?

   A $10c \leq 50$

   B $10c \geq 50$

13. Solve $2(a + 8) > 18$.

   A $a > 1$ C $a > 13$

   B $a > 5$

14. Solve $-40 + 16 \leq 3m + 6$.

   A $m \leq -10$ C $m \leq -6$

   B $m \geq -10$

15. The average of Paula's two test scores must be 80 or more for her to get at least a B in the class. She got a 72 on her first test. What grades can she get on the second test to make at least a B in the class?

   A at least 76   C at least 88

   B at least 84

16. Solve $b + 1 > b + 6$.

   A no solutions

   B all real numbers

17. Solve $\frac{3}{6}x < \frac{1}{6}x + 10$.

   A $x < 6$ C $x < 30$

   B $x < 10$

18. Latisha is on page 30 of her book and reads 3 pages every night. Sal is on page 40 of the same book and reads 2 pages every night. How long will it take Latisha to be further in the book than Sal?

   A 3 nights   C 15 nights

   B 11 nights

19. Solve the compound inequality □ $6 \leq x - 2 < 14$.

   A $4 \leq x < 12$

   B $8 \leq x < 16$

20. Which graph represents the solutions of $p + 1 < -1$ OR $p - 5 > 7$?

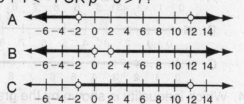

21. Which compound inequality is shown by the graph below?

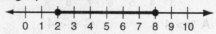

   A $x \geq 2$ AND $x \leq 8$

   B $x \geq 2$ OR $x \leq 8$

Holt McDougal Algebra 1

LESSON 3-1 **Practice A**

Graphing Relationships

For each, write if the height is *rising*, *falling*, or *staying the same*. The first one is done for you.

1.
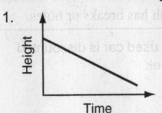

falling

2.
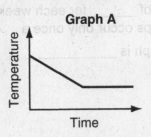

3.
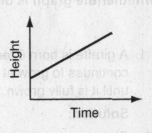

Choose the graph that best represents each situation.

Graph A
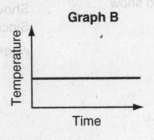

Graph B

Graph C
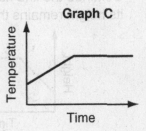

4. The temperature of the water in a glass remained the same.

_____

5. The temperature of the water in a glass rose steadily for several hours, then remained the same.

_____

6. The temperature of the water in a glass cooled down steadily with the addition of ice, then stayed the same when all the ice had melted.

_____

Write a possible situation for the graph. (*Hint:* As the number of subway cars gets greater, what happens to the number of passengers?)

7.
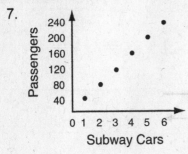

_____

_____

_____

Holt McDougal Algebra 1

LESSON 3-1 Problem Solving
Graphing Relationships

Sketch a graph for the given situation. Tell whether the graph is discrete or continuous.

> **continuous:** graph is unbroken line or smooth curve.
> **discrete:** graph has breaks or holes.

1. A giraffe is born 6 feet tall and continues to grow at a steady rate until it is fully grown.

   Solution:

   Choose a point on the vertical axis to represent 6 ft, the height at birth.

   Draw a line that rises until the giraffe has reached full growth.

   Continue the line horizontally to show its height remains the same.

   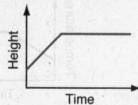

   _____ **continuous**

2. The price of a used car is discounted $200 each week.

   Choose a point on the _____ axis for the original price.

   Show a drop of _____ for each week. Since the drops occur only once a week, the graph is _____.

Choose the graph that best represents the situation.

3. Rebekah turns on the oven and sets it to 300°F. She bakes a tray of cookies and then turns the oven off.

   A Graph 1   C Graph 3

   B Graph 2

4. Leon puts ice cubes in his soup to cool it down before eating it.

   F Graph 1   H Graph 3

   G Graph 2

5. Barlee has the flu and her temperature rises slowly until it reaches 101°F.

   A Graph 1   C Graph 3

   B Graph 2

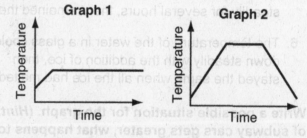

Graph 1   **Graph 2**

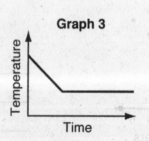

Graph 3

LESSON 3-2 Practice A
Relations and Functions

Express each relation as a table, as a graph, and as a mapping diagram. The first one is started for you.

1. {(–2, 5), (–1, 1), (3, 1), (–1, –2)}

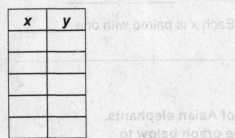

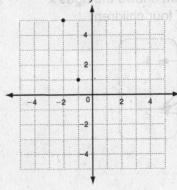

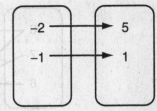

x	y
–2	5
–1	1

2. {(5, 3), (4, 3), (3, 3), (2, 3), (1, 3)}

x	y

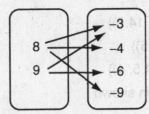

Give the domain and range of each relation. Tell whether the relation is a function. Explain.

3.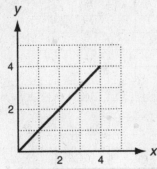

D: _____

R: _____

Function? _____

Explain: _____

_____

_____

_____

4.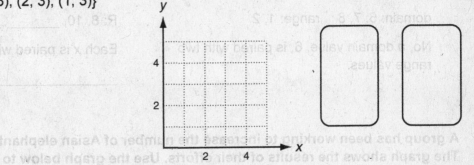

D: _____

R: _____

Function? _____

Explain: _____

_____

_____

_____

LESSON
3-2

Problem Solving
Relations and Functions

Give the domain and range of each relation and tell whether it is a function.

1. The mapping diagram shows the ages *x* and grade level *y* of four children.

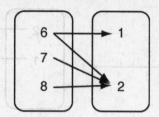

2.

Age x	Shoe Size y
6	8
9	10
12	10
15	10.5
18	11

Solution:

domain: 6, 7, 8   range: 1, 2

No, a domain value, 6, is paired with two range values.

D: 6, 9, _____, _____, _____

R: 8, 10, _____, _____

Each *x* is paired with one _____.

_____

A group has been working to increase the number of Asian elephants. The graph shows the results of their efforts. Use the graph below to answer questions 3–4. Select the correct answer.

3. Which relation represents the information in the graph?

   A {(1, 4.5), (2, 6), (3, 10), (4, 14.5)}

   B {(1, 5), (2, 6), (3, 10), (4, 15)}

   C {(4.5, 1), (6, 2), (10, 3), (14.5, 4)}

4. What is the range of the relation shown in the graph?

   F {0, 1, 2, 3, 4, 5}

   G {1, 2, 3, 4}

   H {5, 6, 10, 15}

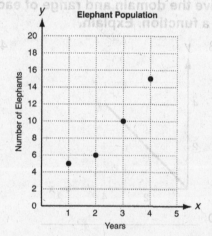

LESSON 3-3 Practice A

Writing Functions

Choose the equation from the box that describes each relationship. The first one is done for you.

1.

x	−3	−2	−1	0
y	−9	−6	−3	0

_____ $y = 3x$ _____

$y = -3x$
$y = 3x$
$y = x - 3$

2. {(3, 0), (2, −1), (1, −2), (0, −3)} _____

3. {(0, 0), (1, −3), (2, −6), (3, −9)} _____

For each, write whether the given variable is *independent* or *dependent*.

4. Auto insurance costs increase with each accident and traffic violation.

- number of accidents/violations: _____

- cost of auto insurance: _____

5. Christian is buying several DVDs that cost $12 each.

- total cost of the DVDs: _____

- number of DVDs purchased: _____

independent: variable whose value does **not** depend on the value of another variable

dependent: variable whose value depends on value of other variable

Evaluate each function for the given input values.

evaluate: find the value of

6. For $f(x) = x + 7$, find $f(x)$ when $x = 3$ and when $x = -5$. _____

7. For $g(x) = -2x$, find $g(x)$ when $x = 4$ and when $x = -1$. _____

8. For $h(x) = 3x - 1$, find $h(x)$ when $x = -2$ and when $x = 7$. _____

Complete the following.

9. Marlena is making beaded bracelets. Each bracelet will have 10 beads. Write a function rule to describe the number of beads she will use. Find a reasonable domain and range for the function if Marlena makes up to 7 bracelets.

rule: _____

domain: _____

range: _____

Holt McDougal Algebra 1

LESSON **Practice A**
Writing Functions

LESSON
3-3
Problem Solving
Writing Functions

Identify the independent and dependent variables.
Write a rule in function notation for each situation.

> **independent:** variable whose value does **not** depend on the value of another variable
> **dependent:** variable whose value depends on the value of another variable

1. Each state receives electoral votes based on the number of representatives it has in the House of Representatives.

Representatives	2	4	6	8
Electoral Votes	4	6	8	10

Solution:

The number of votes is dependent on the number of representatives.

Let r = number of representatives.

$f(r) = r + 2$

2. Terry has 30 baseball cards and gives 2 cards to each of his friends. He wants to know how many cards he'll have left.

Let x = number of friends.

Let $f(x) = 30 -$ _____ where $f(x)$ is number of cards left.

The numbers of cards he has left is _____.

During part of 2005, one American dollar was worth 6 Croatian kuna.
Select the best answer.

3. An American bank wishes to convert d dollars into kuna. Which function rule describes the situation?

  A $f(d) = \dfrac{d}{6}$

  B $f(d) = 6d$

  C $f(d) = \dfrac{6}{d}$

4. Robin converts x dollars into y kuna. Which expression is the independent variable in this situation?

  F x

  G y

  H $6x$

5. Macon has $100 and is thinking about converting some of it into kuna. What is a reasonable range for this situation?

  A $0 \le y \le 6$

  B $0 \le y \le 60$

  C $0 \le y \le 600$

6. Jakov converts n kuna into r dollars. Which expression is the dependent variable in this situation?

  F n

  G r

  H $\dfrac{n}{6}$

Holt McDougal Algebra 1

LESSON 3-4

Practice A

Graphing Functions

Graph the function for the given domain. The first one has been started for you

1. $y = x + 2$; D: $\{-2, -1, 0, 1, 2\}$

x	$y = x + 2$	(x, y)
-2	$y = -2 + 2, y = 0$	$(-2, 0)$

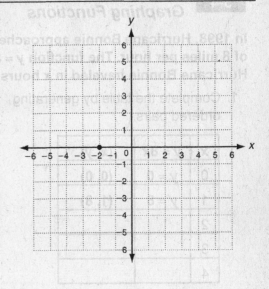

Graph the function. The domain is all real numbers.

2. $y = x^2 \div 2$

x	$y = x^2 \div 2$	(x, y)
0	$y = 0 \div 2, y = 0$	$(0, 0)$

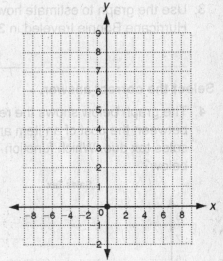

3. The function $y = 8x$ describes how many miles y a salmon swims in x hours. Graph the function. Use the graph to estimate the number of miles the fish swims in 3.5 hours.

x	$y = 8x$	(x, y)

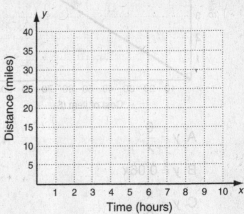

Time (hours)

Holt McDougal Algebra 1

LESSON 3-4

Problem Solving

Graphing Functions

In 1998, Hurricane Bonnie approached the United States at a speed of 8 miles per hour. The function $y = 8x$ describes how many miles y Hurricane Bonnie traveled in x hours.

1. Complete the table by generating ordered pairs.

x	$y = 8x$	(x, y)
0	$y = 0$	$(0, 0)$
1	$y = 8$	$(1, 8)$
2		
3		
4		

2. Graph the function $y = 8x$.

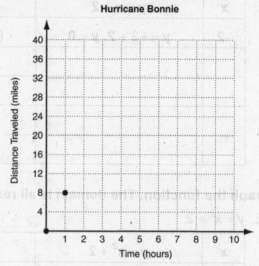

3. Use the graph to estimate how far Hurricane Bonnie traveled in 3.5 hours.

_____

Select the correct answer.

4. The graph below shows the relation between the cost of an item and the sales tax due. Which function is graphed below?

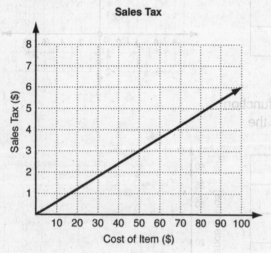

A $y = \dfrac{6}{x}$

B $y = 0.06x$

C $y = \dfrac{x}{6}$

5. The graph below shows the relation between Jeremy's age and the number of times per year he woke up at night. Which function is graphed for the domain {1, 2, 3, 4, 5}?

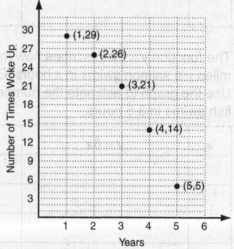

F $y = 30 - x$

G $y = x + 28$

H $y = 30 - x^2$

Holt McDougal Algebra 1

Name _____ Date _____ Class _____

Practice A
Scatter Plots and Trend Lines

1. The table shows the number of soft drinks sold at a small restaurant from 11:00 A.M. to 1:00 P.M. Graph a scatter plot using the given data. The first one has been done for you.

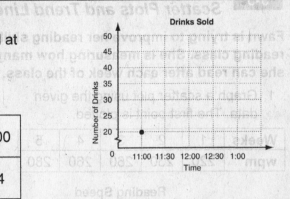

Drinks Sold

Time of Day	11:00	11:30	12:00	12:30	1:00
Number of Drinks	20	29	34	49	44

Complete the following.

2.

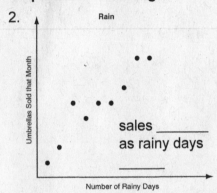

Rain

sales _____ as rainy days

_____

3.

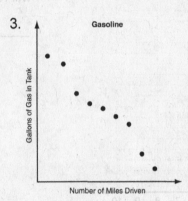

Gasoline

positive: both variables increase
negative: one variable increases, other decreases
none: points are scattered

gas _____

as miles _____

Write *positive*, *negative*, or *none* to describe the correlation you would expect to see between each pair of data sets. Explain.

4. the temperature during the day and the number of people in the swimming pool

_____

_____

5. the height of algebra students and the number of phone calls they make in one week

_____

_____

6. The scatter plot at right shows a relationship between the number of batteries needed and the number of toys. Predict how many batteries will be needed for 11 toys.

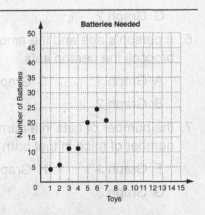

Batteries Needed

_____

Holt McDougal Algebra 1

Name _____ Date _____ Class _____

LESSON 3-5

Problem Solving

Scatter Plots and Trend Lines

Fawn is trying to improve her reading skills by taking a speed-reading class. She is measuring how many words per minute (wpm) she can read after each week of the class.

1. Graph a scatter plot using the given data. The first point is plotted.

Weeks	1	2	3	4	5
wpm	220	230	260	260	280

2. Describe the correlation illustrated by the scatter plot. (*Hint:* Do the points rise or fall?)

_____

_____

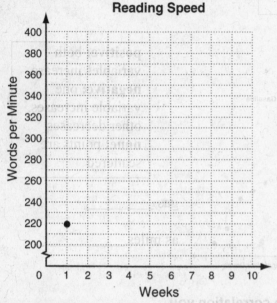

Reading Speed

3. Draw a trend line. Use it to predict the number of words per minute that Fawn will read after 8 weeks of this class.

_____

Choose the scatter plot that best represents the described relationship.

4. the distance a person runs and how physically tired that person is

   A Graph 1   C Graph 3

   B Graph 2

5. the price of a new car and the number of hours in a day

   F Graph 1   H Graph 4

   G Graph 2

6. a person's age and the amount of broccoli the person eats

   A Graph 1   C Graph 3

   B Graph 2

7. the number of cats in a barn and the number of mice in that barn

   F Graph 1   H Graph 4

   G Graph 3

Graph 1   **Graph 2**

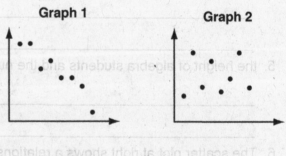

Graph 3   **Graph 4**

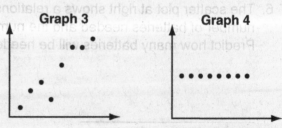

LESSON 3-6 Practice A
Arithmetic Sequences

Determine if the sequence is arithmetic. Write *yes* or *no*.

1. 5, 9, 14, 20, …   2. 10, 22, 34, 46, …

> **arithmetic sequence:** pattern with common differences

_____   _____

Find the common difference for each arithmetic sequence.

3. 12, 15, 18, 21, …   4. 30, 24, 18, 12, …

> **common difference:** same difference from one term to the next

_____   _____

Find the common difference for each arithmetic sequence. Then find the next three terms.

5. 20, 10, 0, −10, …   6. 100, 98, 96, 94, …

_____   _____

Find the requested term for each arithmetic sequence.

7. 42nd term: $a_1 = 10$; $d = 6$ 8. 27th term: 59, 56, 53, 50, …

_____   _____

A swim pass costs $30 for the first month. Each month after that, the cost is $20 per month. Riley wants to swim for 12 months.

9. The sequence for this situation is arithmetic. What is the first term of this sequence? _____

10. What is the common difference? _____

11. The 12th term will be the amount Riley spends for a one year swim pass. Write the equation for finding the total cost of a one year swim pass. _____

Holt McDougal Algebra 1

LESSON 3-6 Problem Solving
Arithmetic Sequences

Find the indicated term of each arithmetic sequence.

1. Darnell has a job and is saving his paychecks each week. How much will Darnell have saved after 11 weeks?

Weeks	1	2	3	4
Savings	$130	$260	$390	$520

Solution:

Common difference: 260 − 130 = 130

130 • 11 = 1430

2. A tube containing 3 ounces of toothpaste is being used at a rate of 0.15 ounces per day. How much toothpaste will be in the tube after one week?

Common difference: _____

0.15 • _____ days in week = _____

3 − 1.05 = _____

The graph below shows the size of Ivor's ant colony over the first four weeks. The ant population will continue to grow at the same rate. Use the graph below to answer questions 3–6. Select the best answer.

3. Which of the following shows how many ants Ivor will have in the next three weeks (weeks 5, 6, 7)?

A 317, 343, 369

B 318, 334, 350

C 319, 345, 371

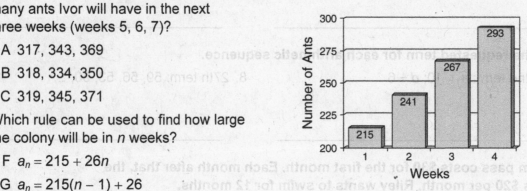

Ivor's Ant Farm

4. Which rule can be used to find how large the colony will be in n weeks?

F $a_n = 215 + 26n$

G $a_n = 215(n - 1) + 26$

H $a_n = 215 + 26(n - 1)$

5. How many ants will Ivor have in 27 weeks?

A 891

B 917

C 5616

6. Ivor's ants weigh 1.5 grams each. How many grams do all of his ants weigh at 13 weeks?

F 683

G 722

H 790.5

Holt McDougal Algebra 1

CHAPTER 3

Functions

Section A Quiz

Select the best answer.

1. Which situation is represented by the graph below?

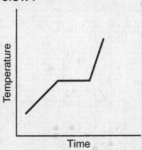

A temperature increases, decreases, then increases rapidly

B temperature decreases, stays constant, then decreases rapidly

C temperature increases, stays constant, then increases rapidly

2. Which of the following is represented by a discrete graph?

F height of a plant growing over time

G number of town visitors each year

H temperature of food while cooking

3. What is the domain and range of the relation below?

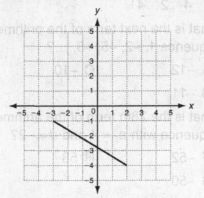

A D: $-4 \leq x \leq -3$ C D: $-3 \leq x \leq 2$
   R: $-1 \leq y \leq 2$ R: $-4 \leq y \leq -1$

B D: $-1 \leq x \leq 2$
   R: $-4 \leq y \leq -3$

4. Which of the following is NOT a function?

F (2, 1), (4, 3), (6, 5), (8, 7)

G (2, 1), (4, 3), (6, 5), (8, 5)

H (2, 1), (4, 3), (6, 5), (2, 7)

5. For $f(x) = 3x - 7$ which represents $f(x)$ when $x = 4$.

A 0   C 14

B 5

6. A cell phone company charges $50 for the phone plus a monthly service charge of $30. Which function gives the total amount for the charges?

F $f(x) = 50 + 30x$ H $f(x) = 50x$

G $f(x) = 30 + 50x$

7. What is the value of $f(x)$ when $x = -3$?

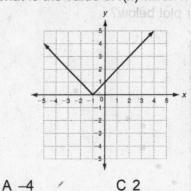

A −4   C 2

B −2

8. Which function is graphed for the domain {−2, −1, 0, 1, 2}?

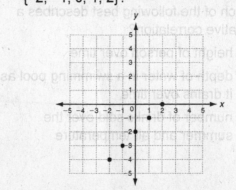

F $f(x) = x - 2$ H $f(x) = 2 - x$

G $f(x) = x + 2$

CHAPTER
3

Functions
Section B Quiz

Select the best answer.

1. Which ordered pairs match the scatter plot below?

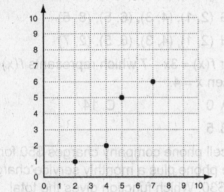

   A (2, 1), (2, 4), (5, 5), (7, 6)

   B (1, 2), (2, 4), (5, 5), (6, 7)

   C (2, 1), (4, 2), (5, 5), (7, 6)

2. Which correlation best describes the scatter plot below?

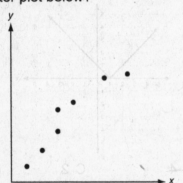

   F Positive   H Continuous

   G Negative

3. Which of the following best describes a negative correlation?

   A height of person over time

   B depth of water in a swimming pool as it drains over time

   C number of drinks sold over the summer and air temperature

4. Based on the graph below, which is the best prediction for the cost of 9 items?

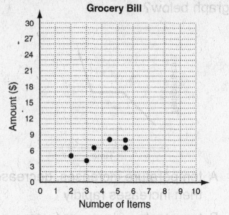

   F about 8   H about 21

   G about 14

5. What is the common difference in the arithmetic sequence −3, −1, 1, 3, …?

   A −3   C 2

   B −2

6. Which of the following is NOT an arithmetic sequence?

   F 2, 2.5, 3, 3.5,…   H −2, 4, −6, 8, …

   G $\frac{1}{4}, \frac{1}{2}, \frac{3}{4}, 1, …$

7. What is the next term of the arithmetic sequence 1, −2, −5, −8, …?

   A −12   C −10

   B −11

8. What is the 28th term of the arithmetic sequence with $a_1 = 4$ and $d = -2$?

   F −52   H 58

   G −50

9. Avery deposited $500 into a savings account in January. She then deposited $100 into the account each month for the remainder of the year. How much money did Avery have in her savings account at the end of December?

   A $1100   C $1600

   B $1200

Holt McDougal Algebra 1

CHAPTER
3

Functions
Chapter Test Form A

Select the best answer.

1. Which situation could be represented by the graph below?

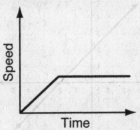

A The speed increases and then decreases.

B The speed increases and then remains constant.

2. Which situation would be represented by a graph with points that are *not connected*?

A The height of a plant as it grows

B The distance traveled on a bike

C The number of shoppers who visited a store each day of the week

3. Which mapping diagram shows the relation {(3, –1), (6, 4), (8, 4)}?

A

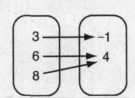

B

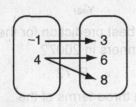

4. What is the domain of the relation below?

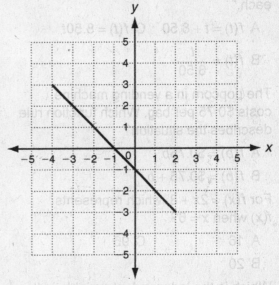

A $-4 \leq x \leq 2$

B $-3 \leq x \leq 3$

5. What is the range of the relation below?

x	3	6	8	9
y	0	5	6	7

A {3, 6, 8, 9}

B {0, 5, 6, 7}

6. Which of the following relations is a function?

A {(1, –6), (3, –5), (1, 0)}

B {(6, 1), (6, 2), (6, 3)}

C {(0, 8), (1, 7), (2, 6)}

7. Which equation shows the relationship between the *x*- and *y*-values below?

x	0	1	2	3	4
y	0	5	10	15	20

A $y = 5x$ C $y = \dfrac{x}{5}$

B $y = x + 4$

Holt McDougal Algebra 1

CHAPTER 3

Functions

Chapter Test Form A continued

8. Which function could represent the following situation: "Tickets cost $8.50 each."

   A $f(t) = t + 8.50$ C $f(t) = 8.50t$

   B $f(t) = \dfrac{t}{8.50}$

9. The popcorn in a vending machine costs $0.75 per bag. Which function rule describes the situation?

   A $f(b) = \$0.75b$

   B $f(b) = \$0.75 + b$

10. For $f(x) = 2x + 8$, which represents $f(x)$ when $x = 6$?

   A 16   C 96

   B 20

11. Which is the independent variable in the following situation?
   "Eliza jogs more often in the summer months than in the winter months."

   A day of the week

   B type of exercise

   C time of year

12. Which function is graphed for the domain $\{-3, -2, -1, 0\}$?

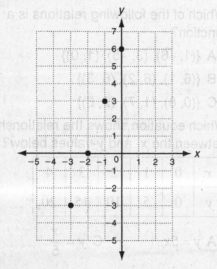

   A $y = 2x + 4$

   B $y = 3x + 6$

13. Which function is graphed below?

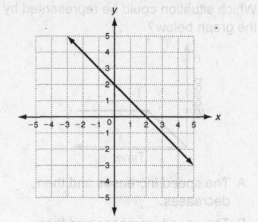

   A $y = 2x$ C $y = 2 - x$

   B $y = 4x$

14. The table shows the number of runners in a race for four years. Draw a scatter plot and trend line.

Year	'02	'03	'04	'05
Number of Runners	21	35	46	50

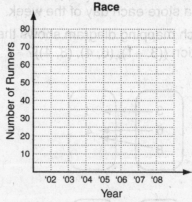

   Which is the best prediction for the number of runners in 2007?

   A 40   B 72

15. Find the next three terms of the arithmetic sequence 3, 7, 11, 15, …

   A 19, 23, 27   B 16, 19, 22

16. What is the 22nd term of the arithmetic sequence 12, 17, 22, 27, …?

   A 105   C 122

   B 117

LESSON 4-1

Practice A

Identifying Linear Functions

Use the graph for Exercises 1–3. The first one is done for you.

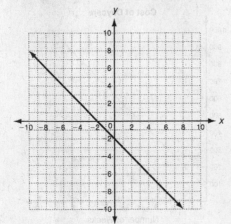

1. Is this graph a function? **yes**

2. Explain how you know it is a function.

   _____

   _____

3. If this graph is a function, is it also a linear function?

   _____

Use the set {(1, 8), (2, 6), (3, 4), (4, 2), (5, 0)} for Exercises 4–5.

4. Does the set of ordered pairs satisfy a linear function? _____

5. Explain how you decided. _____

   _____

6. Write the equation $y = x - 4$ in standard form $(Ax + By = C)$.

   _____

7. Is $y = x - 4$ a linear function?

   _____

8. Graph $y = x - 4$ to check.

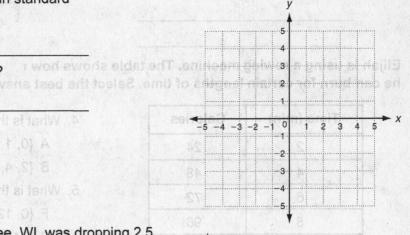

9. In 2005, a storm in Milwaukee, WI, was dropping 2.5 inches of snow every hour. The total amount of snow is given by $f(x) = 2.5x$, where x is the number of hours. Graph this function and give its domain and range.

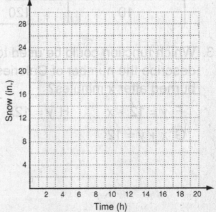

Holt McDougal Algebra 1

Name _____ Date _____ Class _____

Problem Solving
Identifying Linear Functions

Write the correct answer.

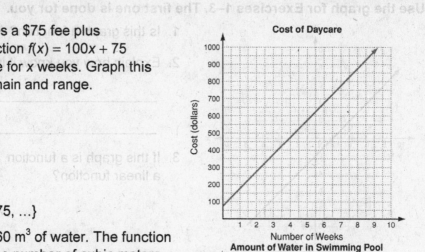

1. A daycare center charges a $75 fee plus $100 per week. The function $f(x) = 100x + 75$ gives the cost of daycare for x weeks. Graph this function and give its domain and range.

   Solution:

   $f(0) = 100 \cdot 0 + 75 = 75$

   $f(1) = 100 \cdot 1 + 75 = 175$

   $f(2) = 100 \cdot 2 + 75 = 275$

   D: {0, 1, 2, 3, ...}

   R: {$75, $175, $275, $375, ...}

2. A swimming pool holds 60 m³ of water. The function $f(x) = 60 - 0.18x$ gives the number of cubic meters of water in the pool, taking into account water lost over x days. Graph this function and give its domain and range.

   $f(0) = 60 - 0.18(0) = 60$

   $f(10) = 60 - 0.18(10) = 58.2$

   $f(60) = 60 - 0.18(60) = 49.2$

   _____

   _____

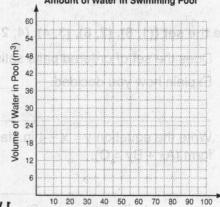

Elijah is using a rowing machine. The table shows how r he can burn for certain lengths of time. Select the best answer.

Time (min)	Calories
2	24
4	48
6	72
8	96
10	120

3. Which function could be used to describe the number of Calories burned after x minutes?

   F $y = 12 + x$ H $y = 12x$

   G $x + y = 12$

4. What is the domain of the function?

   A {0, 1, 2, 3, ...}   C $x \geq 0$

   B {2, 4, 6, ...}

5. What is the range of the function?

   F {0, 12, 24, 36, ...}   H $y \geq 0$

   G {24, 48, 72, ...}   J $y \geq 24$

Holt McDougal Algebra 1

LESSON
4-2

Practice A

Using Intercepts

Find the *x*- and *y*-intercepts. The first one is done for you.

1.
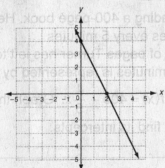

2.
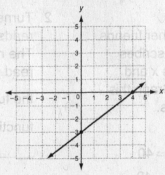

3.
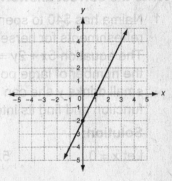

x-intercept: **(y = 0), 2**   *x*-intercept: _____   *x*-intercept: _____

y-intercept: **(x = 0), 4**   *y*-intercept: _____   *y*-intercept: _____

4. Find the intercepts of $2x + 3y = 6$ by following the steps below.

   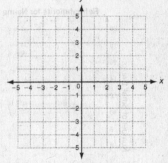

   a. Substitute $y = 0$ into the equation. Solve for *x*.

   _____

   b. The *x*-intercept is: _____

   c. Substitute $x = 0$ into the equation. Solve for *y*.

   _____

   d. The *y*-intercept is: _____

   e. Use the intercepts to graph the line described by the equation.

5. Jennifer started with $50 in her savings account. Each week
   she withdrew $10. The amount of money in her savings account
   after *x* weeks is represented by the function $f(x) = 50 - 10x$.

   a. Find the intercepts and graph the function.

   _____

   b. What does each intercept represent?

   _____

   _____

   _____

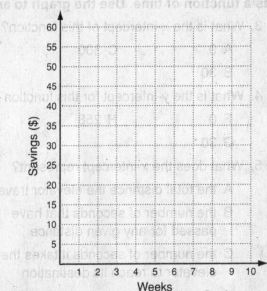

Holt McDougal Algebra 1

LESSON 4-2

Problem Solving
Using Intercepts

Write the correct answer.

1. Naima has $40 to spend on refreshments for herself and her friends. The equation $5x + 2y = 40$ describes the number of large popcorns x and small drinks y she can buy. Graph this function and find its intercepts.

Solution:

Let $x = 0$.
$$5x + 2y = 40$$
$$2y = 40$$
$$y = 20$$
Let $y = 0$.
$$5x + 2y = 40$$
$$5x = 40$$
$$x = 8$$

2. Turner is reading a 400-page book. He reads 4 pages every 5 minutes. The number of pages Turner has left to read after x minutes is represented by the function $f(x) = 400 - \frac{4}{5}x$. Graph this function and find its intercepts.

_____

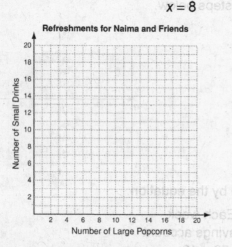

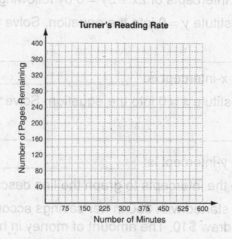

The graph shows the distance of an elevator from its destination as a function of time. Use the graph to answer questions 3–6.

3. What is the x-intercept of this function?

   A 0   C 300

   B 30

4. What is the y-intercept for this function?

   F 0   H 258

   G 30

5. What does the x-intercept represent?

   A the total distance the elevator travels

   B the number of seconds that have passed for any given distance

   C the number of seconds it takes the elevator to reach its destination

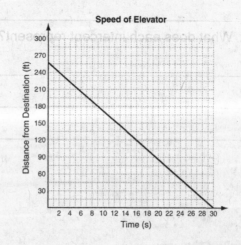

Holt McDougal Algebra 1

LESSON
4-3

Practice A
Rate of Change and Slope

Fill in the blanks to define slope.

1. The _____ is the difference in the *y*-values of two points on a line.

2. The _____ is the difference in the *x*-values of two points on a line.

3. The slope of a line is the ratio of _____ to _____ for any two points on the line.

Find the rise and run between each set of points. Then, write the slope of the line. The first one is done for you.

4.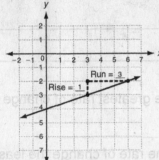

5.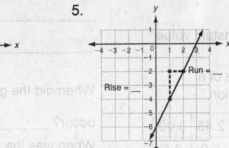

6.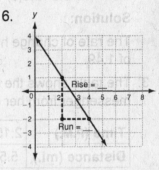

slope = $\dfrac{1}{3}$

slope = _____

slope = _____

Tell whether the slope of each line is positive, negative, zero, or undefined.

7.

8.

9.

_____

_____

_____

10. The table shows a truck driver's distance from home during one day's deliveries. Find the rate of change for each time interval.

Time (h)	0	1	4	5	8	10
Distance (mi)	0	35	71	82	199	200

Hour 0 to Hour 1: _____   Hour 1 to Hour 4: _____   Hour 4 to Hour 5: _____

Hour 5 to Hour 8: _____   Hour 8 to Hour 10: _____

Holt McDougal Algebra 1

Problem Solving

Rate of Change and Slope

Write the correct answer.

1. The table shows the cost per pound of apples.

Weight (lb)	1	2	3	4
Cost ($)	1.49	2.98	4.47	5.96

Describe the rate(s) of change shown.

Solution:

The rate of change has a constant value of 1.49.

2. The table shows Gabe's height on his birthday for five years. Find the rate of change during each time interval.

Age	9	11	12	13	15
Height (in.)	58	59.5	61.5	65	69

_____

_____

When did the greatest rate of change

occur? _____

When was the rate of change the least?

_____

3. The table shows the distance of a messenger from her destination.

Time (P.M.)	2:15	2:30	2:45	3:00
Distance (mi.)	5.5	5.5	5.0	0.5

What is the rate of change from 2:15 P.M. to 2:30 P.M.? What does this rate of change mean?

During which two time periods were the rates of change the same?

_____

_____

_____

The graph below tracks regular gasoline prices from July 2004 to December 2004. Use the graph to answer questions 4–6.

4. What is the slope of the line from November to December?

   A –4   C –0.01

   B –0.04

5. During which time interval did the cost decrease at the greatest rate?

   F Jul to Aug   H Sep to Oct

   G Aug to Sep

6. During which time interval was the slope positive?

   A Jul to Aug   C Sep to Oct

   B Aug to Sep

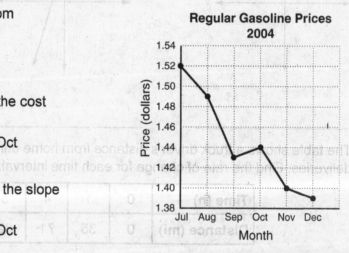

Regular Gasoline Prices 2004

Holt McDougal Algebra 1

Name _____ Date _____ Class_____

Practice A
The Slope Formula

Find the slope of the line that contains each pair of points. The first one is done for you.

1. (3, 1) and (9, 2)

$$m = \frac{y_2 - y_1}{x_2 - x_1}$$

$$= \frac{2-1}{\boxed{9}-\boxed{3}} = \frac{1}{\boxed{6}}$$

2. (–2, 3) and (2, –1)

$$m = \frac{y_2 - y_1}{x_2 - x_1}$$

$$= \frac{-1-\boxed{}}{2-\boxed{}} = \frac{\boxed{}}{\boxed{}} = \boxed{}$$

3. (4, 6) and (0, –2)

$$m = \frac{y_2 - y_1}{x_2 - x_1}$$

$$= \frac{\boxed{}-\boxed{}}{\boxed{}-\boxed{}} = \frac{\boxed{}}{\boxed{}} = \boxed{}$$

Each graph or table shows a linear relationship. Find the slope.

4.

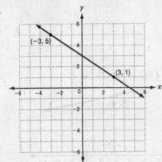

5.

x	y
0	82
3	76
6	70
9	64
12	58

_____

_____

Find the slope of each line. Then tell what the slope represents.

6.

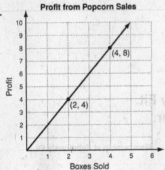

7.

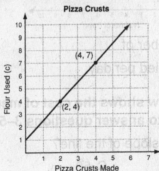

_____

_____

_____

_____

Complete the steps to find the slope of the line described by 2x + 5y = –10.

8. a. Find the x-intercept.

Let $y = 0$

$2x + 5\,(\underline{}) = -10$

$\underline{} = -10$

$\div\underline{} \quad \div\underline{}$

$x = \underline{}$

b. Find the y-intercept.

Let $x = 0$

$2\,(\underline{}) + 5y = -10$

$\underline{} = -10$

$\div\underline{} \quad \div\underline{}$

$y = \underline{}$

c. The line contains (____, 0)

and (0, ____). Use the

slope formula.

$$m = \frac{y_2 - y_1}{x_2 - x_1}$$

$$= \frac{\boxed{}-0}{0-\boxed{}} = \frac{\boxed{}}{\boxed{}}$$

Name _____ Date _____ Class_____

Problem Solving
The Slope Formula

Write the correct answer.

1. The graph shows the number of emergency kits assembled by volunteers over a period of days. Find the slope of the line. Then tell what the slope represents.

   Solution:

   $$slope = \frac{y_2 - y_1}{x_2 - x_1}$$

   $$slope = \frac{72 - 24}{6 - 2} = \frac{48}{4} = 12$$

   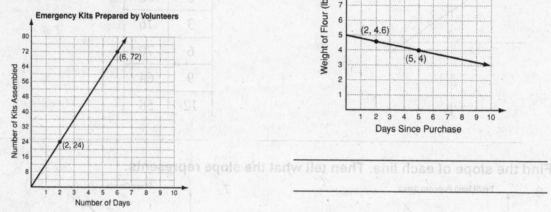

   Emergency Kits Prepared by Volunteers

   12; the number of kits assembled per day

2. The graph shows how much flour is in a bag at different times. Find the slope of the line. Then tell what the slope represents. Use the slope formula

   $$\frac{y_2 - y_1}{x_2 - x_1}.$$

   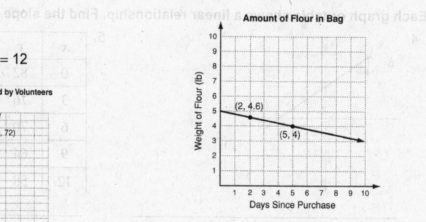

   Amount of Flour in Bag

   _____

   _____

The graph below shows the cost of membership at Fabulously Fit. Use the graph to answer questions 3–5. Select the best answer.

3. What is the slope of the line?

   A 24   C 50

   B 35

4. What does the slope represent?

   F the late payment fee

   G the total cost of membership

   H the monthly membership fee

5. A second line is graphed that shows the cost of membership at The Fitness Studio. The line contains (0, 35) and (5, 85). What is the slope of this line?

   A 10   C 45

   B 20

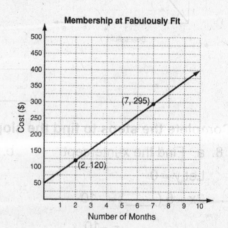

Membership at Fabulously Fit

Holt McDougal Algebra 1

LESSON 4-5

Practice A

Direct Variation

Complete the table. The first one is done for you.

	Solve for y (if needed).	Is the equation in the form y = kx?	Is it a direct variation?	Constant of variation
1. $y = 7x$	$y = 7x$	yes	yes	7
2. $y = 4x - 10$				
3. $5x - 2y = 0$				

Complete the table.

	Find the value of $\frac{y}{x}$ for each ordered pair.	Is the value of $\frac{y}{x}$ the same for each ordered pair?	Direct variation?
4.			
5.			

4.
x	10	15	20
y	2	3	4

5.
x	4	8	12
y	16	20	24

6. The value of y varies directly with x, and $y = -2$ when $x = -4$.
Find y when $x = 8$.

Find k:

$y = kx$

$-2 = k(-4)$

_____ = k

Use k to find y:

$y = kx$

$y = (\_\_\_)(\_\_\_)$

$y = _____$

7. The value of y varies directly with x, and $y = 12$ when $x = 8$.
Find y when $x = 15$.

Find k:

$y = kx$

$12 = k(8)$

_____ = k

Use k to find y:

$y = kx$

$y = (\_\_\_)(\_\_\_)$

$y = _____$

Holt McDougal Algebra 1

Problem Solving
Direct Variation

Write the correct answer.

1. Wesley earns $6.50 per hour. The total amount of his paycheck varies directly with the number of hours he works. Write a direct variation equation for the amount of money y Wesley earns for working x hours.

   Solution:

   $y = 6.5x$

2. The equation $-4x + y = 0$ relates the number of pages in a photo album x to the number of pictures in the album y. Tell whether the relationship is a direct variation. Explain your answer.

   _____

   _____

3. The formula $9x - 5y = -160$ relates the temperature in degrees Fahrenheit y to the temperature in degrees Celsius x. Tell whether the relationship is a direct variation. Explain your answer.

   _____

   _____

4. The number of miles driven varies directly with the number of gallons of gas used. Erin drove 297 miles on 9 gallons of gas. How far would she be able to drive on 14 gallons of gas?

   _____

   _____

Select the best answer.

5. The table shows the relationship between the number of lemons and their cost.

Lemons x	1	2	3	4
Cost y	0.1	0.2	0.3	0.4

   Is the relationship a direct variation?

   A Yes; it can be written as $y = 0.1x$.

   B Yes; it can be written as $y = 10x$.

   C No; it cannot be written as $y = kx$.

7. The Diaz family is driving at a constant speed on the highway so their distance varies directly with their speed. They traveled 17.5 miles in 15 minutes. How far did they travel in 2 hours?

   A 50 miles   C 140 miles

   B 70 miles

6. The table shows the relationship between the hours since sunrise and the temperature in degrees Celsius.

Hour x	1	2	3	4
Temp. y	25	26	28	32

   Is the relationship a direct variation?

   F Yes; it can be written as $y = 25x$.

   G Yes; it can be written as $y = 8x$.

   H No; it cannot be written as $y = kx$.

LESSON 4-6

Practice A
Slope-Intercept Form

**Write the equation that describes each line in slope-intercept form.
The first one is done for you.**

1. slope = $\dfrac{2}{3}$; *y*-intercept = 2

   $y = \underline{\dfrac{2}{3}}\, x + \underline{\ 2\ }$

2. slope = –1; *y*-intercept = –8

   $y = \underline{\hspace{1cm}} x - \underline{\hspace{1cm}}$

3. slope = –2, (3, 5) is on the line.
   Find the *y*-intercept: $y = mx + b$

   $5 = (-2)(\underline{\hspace{0.8cm}}) + b$
   $5 = \underline{\hspace{1cm}} + b$
   $+ \underline{\hspace{0.8cm}} + \underline{\hspace{0.8cm}}$
   $\underline{\hspace{0.8cm}} = b$

   Write the equation: $y = \underline{\hspace{1cm}} x + \underline{\hspace{1cm}}$

Write each equation in slope-intercept form. Then graph the line.

4. $y - 2x = -4$

   $\underline{\hspace{2cm} y = 2x - 4 \hspace{2cm}}$

   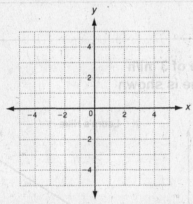

5. $y - 3 = -\dfrac{1}{2}x$

   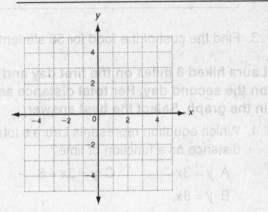

6. A school orders 25 desks for each classroom,
   plus 30 spare desks. The total number ordered
   as a function of the number of classrooms is shown
   in the graph.

   a. Write the equation represented by the graph.

   _____

   b. Identify the slope and *y*-intercept and describe their

   meanings. _____

   _____

   c. Find the total number of desks ordered if there are
   24 classrooms.

   _____

   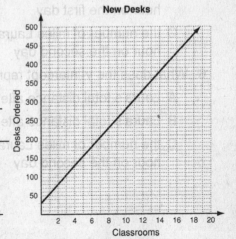

Holt McDougal Algebra 1

Problem Solving

LESSON 4-6

Slope-Intercept Form

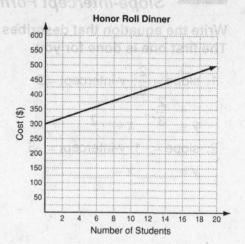

Honor Roll Dinner

The cost of food for an honor roll dinner is $300 plus $10 per student. The cost of the food as a function of the number of students is shown in the graph. Write the correct answer.

1. Write an equation that represents the cost as a function of the number of students.

   Solution:

   Let y = cost.

   Let x = number of students.

   $y = 10x + 300$

2. Identify the slope and y-intercept and describe their meanings.

   _____

   _____

3. Find the cost of the food for 50 students. _____

Laura hiked 8 miles on the first day and is hiking at a rate of 3 mi/h on the second day. Her total distance as a function of time is shown in the graph. Select the best answer.

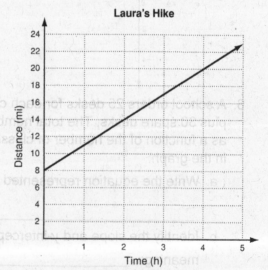

Laura's Hike

4. Which equation represents Laura's total distance as a function of time?

   A $y = 3x$ C $y = 3x + 8$

   B $y = 8x$

5. What does the slope represent?

   A Laura's total distance after two day

   B the number of miles Laura hiked per hour on the first day

   C the number of miles Laura hikes per hour on the second day

6. What does the y-intercept represent?

   A Laura's total distance after one day

   B Laura's total distance after two days

   C the number of miles Laura hikes per hour on the second day

Holt McDougal Algebra 1

Practice A
Point-Slope Form

**Match each graph with the correct slope and point.
The first one is done for you.**

1. slope = $\frac{1}{2}$; (0, 2) ___C___   2. slope = $-\frac{1}{2}$; (2, 0) _____   3. slope = –2; (2, 0) _____

A 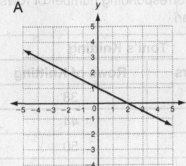   B 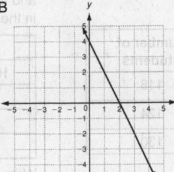   C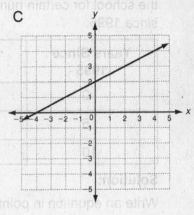

**Write an equation in point-slope form for the line with the given slope
that contains the given point. The first one is done for you.**

4. slope = 4; (3, 8)

5. slope = $-\frac{1}{2}$; (5, –3)

$$y - 8 = 4(x - 3)$$

**Write an equation in slope-intercept form for the line with the given
slope that contains the given point. The first one is done for you.**

6. slope = 5; (1, 7)

7. slope = –3; (4, 0)

$$y = 5x + 2$$

**Find the slope of the line that contains the given points. Then write an
equation in slope-intercept form for the line. The first one is done for you.**

8. (0, 2); (2, 6)

9. (8, –2); (4, –4)

$$2;\ y = 2x + 2$$

Holt McDougal Algebra 1

LESSON 4-7
Problem Solving
Point-Slope Form

Write the correct answer.

1. The number of students in a school has been increasing at a constant rate. The table shows the number of students in the school for certain numbers of years since 1995.

Years Since 1995	Number of Students
0	118
5	124
10	130

Solution:

Write an equation in point-slope form that represents this linear function.

$y - 130 = 1.2(x - 10)$

Write the equation in slope-intercept form.

$y = 1.2x + 118$

Assuming the rate of change remains constant, how many students will be in the school in 2010?

$y = 1.2(15) + 118$

$y = 136$

2. Toni is finishing a scarf at a constant rate. The table shows the number of hours Toni has spent knitting this week and the corresponding number of rows in the scarf.

Toni's Knitting	
Hours	Rows of Knitting
2	38
4	44
6	50

Write an equation in slope-intercept form that represents this linear function.

_____

The cost of a cell phone for one month is a linear function of the number of minutes used. The total cost for 20, 35, and 40 additional minutes are shown. Select the best answer.

3. What is the slope of the line represented in the table?

   A 0.1   C 2

   B 0.4

Cell-Phone Costs			
Number of Additional Minutes	20	35	40
Total Cost	$48	$54	$56

4. What would be the monthly cost if 60 additional minutes were used?

   A $64   C $84

   B $72

5. What does the *y*-intercept of the function represent?

   A total cost of the bill

   B number of additional minutes used

   C cost with no additional minutes used

Holt McDougal Algebra 1

LESSON 4-8 Practice A

Line of Best Fit

1. The data in the table are graphed at the right along with two lines of fit. Part a is done for you.

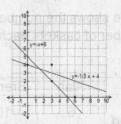

x	0	3	3	6
y	4	2	4	0

a. Find the residuals for $y = -x + 5$. __1, 0, –2, –1__

b. Find the sum of the squares of the residuals for
$y = -x + 5$._____

c. Find the residuals for $y = -\frac{1}{3}x + 4$._____

d. Find the sum of the squares of the residuals for
$y = -\frac{1}{3}x + 4$._____

e. Which line is a better fit for the data?_____

> **residuals:**
> vertical distances from points to line of fit

2. Use the data in the table to answer the questions that follow.

x	2	4	5	7	10
y	4.3	4.8	5.1	5.75	6.4

a. Find an equation for a line of best fit. _____

b. What is the value of the correlation coefficient?_____

c. How well does the line represent the data? _____

d. Describe the correlation. _____

> **correlation coefficient:**
> a number r between –1 and

3. Use the data in the table to answer the questions that follow.

x	10	8	6	4	2
y	3	3.2	3.5	3.8	4

a. Find an equation for a line of best fit. _____

b. What is the value of the correlation coefficient? _____

c. How well does the line represent the data? _____

d. Describe the correlation. _____

Holt McDougal Algebra 1

LESSON 4-8

Problem Solving
Line of Best Fit

1. The table shows the number of hours different players practice basketball each week and the number of baskets each player scored during a game.

Player	Alan	Brenda	Caleb	Shawna	Fernando	Gabriela
Hours Practiced	5	10	7	2	0	21
Baskets Scored	6	11	8	4	2	19

a. Find an equation for a line of best fit. Round decimals to the nearest tenth.

Solution: Use a calculator to find the equation for the line of best fit: $y = 0.8x + 2.3$
_____

b. Interpret the meaning of the slope and *y*-intercept.

Solution: Slope: for each hour practiced, a player will score 0.8 baskets;
_____

y-intercept: a player who practices 0 *h* will score 2.3 baskets.
_____

Select the best answer.

2. Use the equation above to predict the number of baskets scored by a player who practices 40 hours a week. Round to the nearest whole number.

   A 32 baskets

   B 33 baskets

   C 34 baskets

3. Which is the best description of the correlation?

   F strong positive

   G weak positive

   H weak negative

4. Given the data, what advice can you give to a player who wants to increase the number of baskets he or she scores during a game?

   A Practice more hours per week.

   B Practice fewer hours per week.

   C Practice the same hours per week.

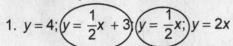

LESSON
4-9

Practice A

Slopes of Parallel and Perpendicular Lines

Circle the equations whose lines are parallel. The first one is done for you.

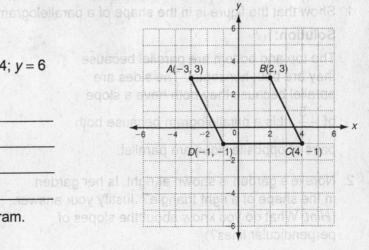

1. $y = 4$; $\left(y = \dfrac{1}{2}x + 3\right)$ $\left(y = \dfrac{1}{2}x\right)$; $y = 2x$

2. $y - 5 = 6(x + 2)$; $y = -6x$; $6x + y = 4$; $y = 6$

3. Find the slope of each segment.

   slope of $\overline{AB}$: _____

   slope of $\overline{AD}$: _____

   slope of $\overline{DC}$: _____

   slope of $\overline{BC}$: _____

   Explain why *ABCD* is a parallelogram.

   _____

   _____

Circle the equations whose lines are perpendicular. The first one is done for you.

4. $(y = x - 4)$; $y = 3$; $(y = -x)$; $y = -3$

5. $y = 5x + 1$; $y = 3$; $y = \dfrac{1}{5}x$; $x = 5$

6. $y = \dfrac{1}{3}x - 2$; $x = 2$; $y - 4 = 3(x + 3)$; $y = -3x + 9$

7. Find the slope of each segment.

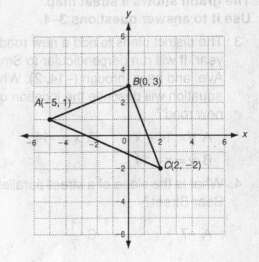

   slope of $\overline{AB}$: _____

   slope of $\overline{BC}$: _____

   slope of $\overline{AC}$: _____

   Explain why *ABC* is a right triangle.
   (*Hint:* What do perpendicular lines form?)

   _____

   _____

LESSON 4-9

Problem Solving

Slopes of Parallel and Perpendicular Lines

Write the correct answer.

1. Show that the figure is in the shape of a parallelogram.

   Solution:

   The top and bottom are parallel because they are both horizontal. The sides are parallel because they both have a slope of $-\frac{5}{3}$. It is a parallelogram because both pairs of opposite sides are parallel.

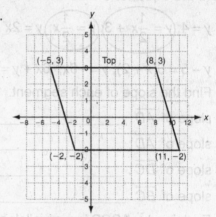

2. Norelle's garden is shown at right. Is her garden in the shape of a right triangle? Justify your answer. (*Hint:* What do you know about the slopes of perpendicular lines?)

   _____

   _____

   _____

   _____

Norelle's Garden

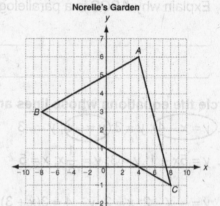

The graph shows a street map. Use it to answer questions 3–4.

3. The district plans to add a new road next year. It will run perpendicular to Smith Ave. and pass through (−14, 2). What equation will describe the location of the new road?

   A $y = 14 - x$ C $x = -14$

   B $y = x - 14$

4. What is the slope of a street parallel to Bear Street?

   A −7   C $\frac{1}{7}$

   B $-\frac{1}{7}$

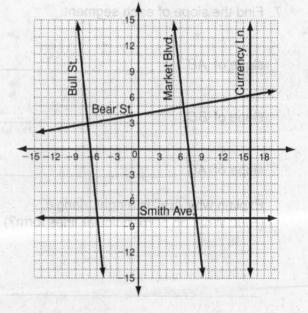

Holt McDougal Algebra 1

LESSON 4-10

Practice A

Transforming Linear Functions

Fill in each blank with *translation*, *rotation*, or *reflection*. The first one is done for you.

1. A ____rotation____ is like a *turn*.

2. A _____ is like a *slide*.

3. A _____ is like a *flip*.

Graph *f(x)* and *g(x)*. Then describe the transformation(s) from the graph of *f(x)* to the graph of *g(x)*.

4. $f(x) = x$; $g(x) = x + 5$

_____

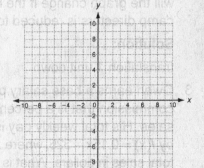

5. $f(x) = 2x - 1$; $g(x) = 4x - 1$

_____

6. $f(x) = x$; $g(x) = \frac{1}{2}x - 7$

_____

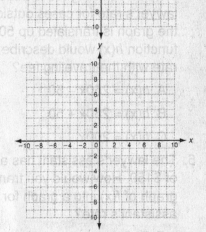

7. The cost of making a ceramic picture frame at a pottery store is $12, plus $5 per hour while you paint. The total cost for the frame that you spend *x* hours painting is $f(x) = 5x + 12$.

   a. How will the graph of this function change if the cost of the frame is raised to $15?

_____

   b. How will the graph of this function change if the hourly charge is lowered to $4?

_____

Holt McDougal Algebra 1

Name _____ Date _____ Class _____

Problem Solving
Transforming Linear Functions

Write the correct answer.

1. At a camp there must be 1 counselor for every 8 campers, plus 3 camp directors. The function describing the number of counselors is $f(x) = \frac{1}{8}x + 3$ where x is the number of campers. How will the graph change if the number of camp directors is reduced to 2?

    Solution:

    translation 1 unit down

2. A city water service has a base cost of $12 per month plus $1.50 per hundred cubic feet (HCF) of water. Write a function $f(x)$ to represent the cost of water as a function of x, amount used. Then write a second function $g(x)$ to represent the cost if the rate rises to $1.60 per HCF.

    _____

    _____

    How would the graph of $g(x)$ compare to the graph of $f(x)$?

    _____

    _____

3. Owen earns a base salary plus a commission that is a percent of his total sales. His total weekly pay is described by $f(x) = 0.15x + 325$, where x is his total sales in dollars. What is the change in Owen's salary plan if his total weekly pay function changes to $g(x) = 0.20x + 325$?

    _____

    _____

A lawyer charges $250 per hour. The graph represents the cost of the lawyer as a function of time. Select the best answer.

4. When a traveling fee is added to the lawyer's rate for cases outside the city, the graph is translated up 50 units. What function $h(x)$ would describe the lawyer's rate with the traveling fee?

    A $h(x) = 250x - 50$

    B $h(x) = 250x + 50$

    C $h(x) = 200x$

5. The lawyer's assistant has an hourly rate of $150. How would you transform the graph of $f(x)$ into a graph for the assistant's rate?

    F Reflect it over the y-axis.

    G Translate it down 100 units.

    H Rotate it clockwise about $(0, 0)$.

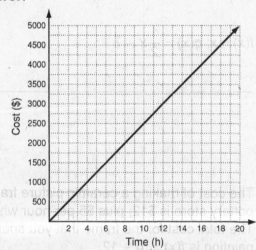

6. Which hourly rate would NOT make the graph steeper?

    A $225   C $300

    B $275

Holt McDougal Algebra 1

CHAPTER 4

Linear Functions

Section A Quiz

Select the best answer.

1. Which of the following is a linear function?

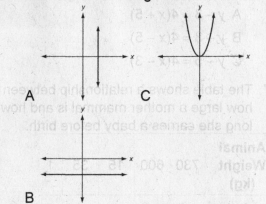

2. Which of the functions below is a linear function?

   A $y = x - 7$ C $y = |x| - 7$

   B $y = x^2 - 7$

3. What are the *x*- and *y*-intercepts of the line graphed below?

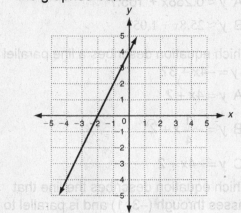

   A *x*-int: 4, *y*-int: –2
   B *x*-int: –2, *y*-int: 4
   C *x*-int: –4, *y*-int: 2

4. What is the *x*-intercept of $4x + 2y = 6$?

   A $\frac{1}{3}$ C $\frac{3}{2}$

   B $\frac{2}{3}$

5. What is the slope of a vertical line?

   A positive   C undefined
   B negative

6. What is the slope of the line below?

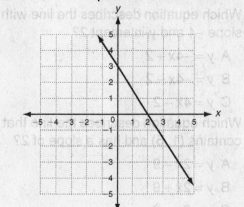

   A $-\frac{3}{2}$ C $\frac{2}{3}$

   B $-\frac{2}{3}$

7. What is the slope of the line containing the ordered pair (2, 3) and (–4, 0)?

   A –2   C $\frac{1}{2}$

   B $-\frac{1}{2}$

8. Is the equation $2x + 8 = y$ a direct variation?

   A yes
   B no

9. The equation $2x + 5y = 0$ is a direct variation. What is the constant of variation?

   A $-\frac{5}{2}$ C $\frac{2}{5}$

   B $-\frac{2}{5}$

10. If the value of *y* varies directly with *x*, and $y = 4$ when $x = -10$, find *y* when $x = 35$.

    A –350   C –14

    B –140

Linear Functions

Section B Quiz

Select the best answer.

1. Which equation describes the line with slope –4 and y-intercept 2?

   A $y = -4x + 2$

   B $y = -4x - 2$

   C $y = 4x - 2$

2. Which equation describes the line that contains (1, 5) and has a slope of 2?

   A $y = 2x - 9$

   B $y = 2x + 9$

   C $y = 2x + 3$

3. What are the slope and y-intercept of the line described by $y = 3x - 6$?

   A $m = -3; b = -6$

   B $m = 3; b = -6$

   C $m = -6; b = 3$

4. Which equation describes the line that passes through (2, 1) and (0, –5)?

   A $y = \frac{1}{3}x - 5$

   B $y = 3x - 5$

   C $y = -\frac{1}{3}x - 5$

5. Which equation describes the line passing through (4, –2) with a slope of $\frac{1}{2}$?

   A $y = \frac{1}{2}x - 2$

   B $y = \frac{1}{2}x - 4$

   C $y = \frac{1}{2}x + 4$

6. Which equation goes through the point (3, 5) and has a slope of 4?

   A $y - 3 = 4(x + 5)$

   B $y + 3 = 4(x - 5)$

   C $y - 5 = 4(x - 3)$

7. The table shows a relationship between how large a mother mammal is and how long she carries a baby before birth.

Animal Weight (kg)	730	600	15	35	1
Gestation Period (days)	284	270	150	148	33

   Which equation could represent a line of best fit for this data?

   A $y \approx 0.258x + 105.7$

   B $y \approx 25.8x + 1{,}057$

8. Which equation describes a line parallel to $y = -4x + 3$?

   A $y = 4x + 2$

   B $y = -\frac{1}{4}x + 2$

   C $y = -4x + 2$

9. Which equation describes the line that passes through (–3, 1) and is parallel to the line described by $y = 4x + 1$?

   A $y = 4x + 13$

   B $y = -\frac{1}{4}x + \frac{1}{4}$

   C $y = 4x - 11$

10. Which equation describes a line perpendicular to $y = 3x - 5$?

   A $y = \frac{1}{3}x - 3$

   B $y = 3x - 3$

   C $y = -\frac{1}{3}x - 3$

Name _____ Date _____ Class _____

Linear Functions
Chapter Test Form A

Select the best answer.

1. Which graph represents a linear function?

   A
   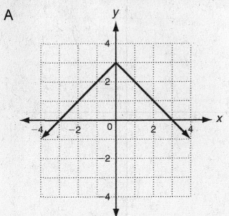

   B
   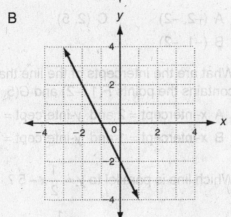

2. A car travels at 60 mi/h. The function $f(x) = 60x$ gives the distance the car travels in x hours. What is the range of this function?

   A $y \geq 0$

   B $\{0, 1, 2, 3, ...\}$

   C $\{0, 60, 120, 180, ...\}$

3. Find the x-intercept of the equation $x + 5y = 20$.

   A 4

   B 5

   C 20

4. The table shows the price of a video game for different years since the game was released. During which time interval did the price decrease at the greatest rate?

Year	2000	2002	2003	2005	2007
Price ($)	58	54	50	44	43

   A 2000 to 2002   C 2003 to 2005

   B 2002 to 2003

5. The slope of this line is _____.

   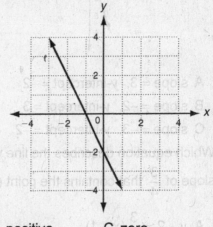

   A positive   C zero

   B negative

6. Find the slope of the line that contains the points (6, 8) and (2, 1).

   A $\dfrac{7}{4}$ B $\dfrac{9}{8}$

7. Is this relationship a direct variation?

x	−3	2	1
y	−4	6	4

   A yes   B no

8. Which equation describes the line with a slope of 2 and y-intercept of 6?

   A $y = 2x + 6$ B $y = 6x + 2$

Holt McDougal Algebra 1

9. What is the slope and y-intercept of the graph?

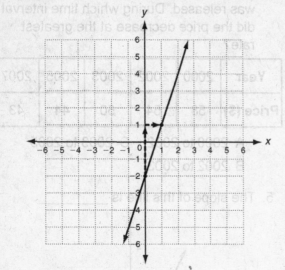

   A slope = 3, y-intercept = –2

   B slope = –2, y-intercept = 3

   C slope = –3, y-intercept = –2

10. Which equation describes the line with a slope of $\frac{3}{4}$ that contains the point (1, –2)?

   A $y - 2 = \frac{3}{4}(x + 1)$

   B $y + 2 = \frac{3}{4}(x - 1)$

11. The table shows the relationship between the size of a painting by a particular artist, and the price they charge for the painting.

Painting Size (in²)	48	64	144	48	100
Price (dollars)	100	150	300	85	200

Which equation could represent a line of best fit for this data?

   A $y \approx 2.09x - 1.95$

   B $y \approx 209x - 195$

12. Graph $y - 2 = 3(x - 1)$. Which point is on the graph?

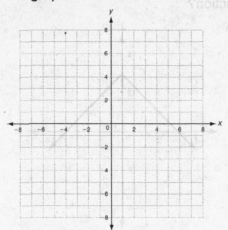

   A (–2, –2)   C (2, 5)

   B (–1, –2)

13. What are the intercepts of the line that contains the points F(1, –2) and G(5, 6)?

   A x-intercept = 2 and y-intercept = –4

   B x-intercept = 1 and y-intercept = –1

14. Which line is parallel to $y = \frac{1}{2}x - 5$?

   A $y = -2x$ C $y = \frac{1}{2}x - 3$

   B $y = -\frac{1}{2}x + 1$

15. Which equation describes a line that passes through (0, 3) and is perpendicular to the line described by $y = -5x - 4$?

   A $y = -5x + 3$ C $y = \frac{1}{5}x + 3$

   B $y = -\frac{1}{5}x + 3$

Holt McDougal Algebra 1

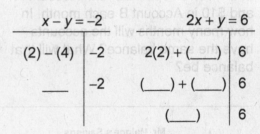

LESSON 5-1 Practice A
Solving Systems by Graphing

Is the ordered pair a solution of the given system? Circle *yes* or *no* for each equation. Then, write *is* or *is not* to complete the sentence. The first one is done for you.

1. $(1, -2);$ $\begin{cases} 2x + y = 0 \\ x + 4y = -7 \end{cases}$

$2x + y = 0$		$x + 4y = -7$	
$2(1) + (-2)$	0	$(1) + 4(\underline{-2})$	-7
$(\underline{2}) + (-2)$	0	$(\underline{1}) + (\underline{-8})$	-7
$(\underline{0})$	0	$(\underline{-7})$	-7

(yes) or no   (yes) or no

$(1, -2)$ _____**is**_____ a solution of the system.

2. $(2, 4);$ $\begin{cases} x - y = -2 \\ 2x + y = 6 \end{cases}$

$x - y = -2$		$2x + y = 6$	
$(2) - (4)$	-2	$2(2) + (\underline{})$	6
___	-2	$(\underline{}) + (\underline{})$	6
		$(\underline{})$	6

yes or no   yes or no

$(2, 4)$ _____ a solution of the system.

Solve each system by graphing. One of the lines has been graphed for you.

3. $\begin{cases} y = 3x - 5 \\ y = x - 3 \end{cases}$ Solution : _____

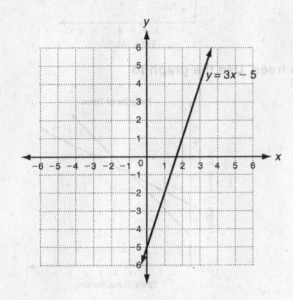

4. The Science Club wants to rent a bus. Main Street Buses charges a $40 rental fee, plus $2 per mile. County Bus Line charges a $20 rental fee, plus $3 per mile. For what number of miles will the total charge be the same? What will that charge be?

(*Hint:* Set up two equations.)

_____

LESSON 5-1 **Problem Solving**

Solving Systems by Graphing

Write the correct answer. The first two have been started for you.

1. Mr. Malone puts money in two savings accounts.
Account A started with $200.
Account B started with $300.
Mr. Malone deposits $15 in Account A and $10 in Account B each month. In how many months will the accounts have the same balance? What will that balance be?

_____

2. Tom has 5 comic books in his collection and receives 5 new comic books each month. Joe has 145 comic books, but sends 5 to each of his 3 friends each month. In how many months will they have the same number of comic books? How many books will that be?

_____

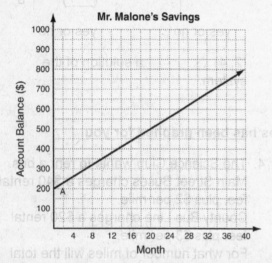

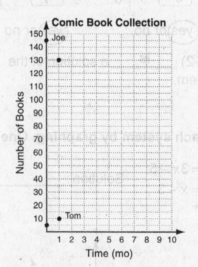

The graph below compares the heights of two trees. Use the graph to answer questions 3–5. Select the best answer.

3. How many years after planting will the trees be the same height?

   A 1 years   C 4 years

   B 2 years

4. Which system of equations is represented by the graph?

   F $\begin{cases} y = x + 2 \\ y = 0.5x + 2 \end{cases}$ H $\begin{cases} y = 2x + 4 \\ y = x + 4 \end{cases}$

   G $\begin{cases} y = x + 2 \\ y = 0.5x + 4 \end{cases}$

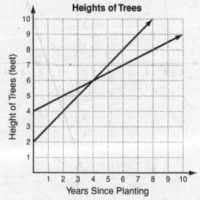

5. How fast does the tree that started at 2 feet tall grow?

   A 0.5 ft/yr   C 1.5 ft/yr

   B 1 ft/yr

Holt McDougal Algebra 1

Practice A

Solving Systems by Substitution

Fill in the blanks to solve each system by substitution.
The first one is started for you.

1. $\begin{cases} y = 3x \\ y = x + 4 \end{cases}$

   Substitute _____**3x**_____ for y in the second equation.

   _____**3x**_____ $= x + 4$

   $-$ **x**   **$-x$**

   _____ $= 4$

   $\div$ _____ $\div$ _____

   _____ $=$ _____

   Since $x =$ _____, substitute _____ for x in one of the equations to find the value of y:

   $y = 3x$

   $y = 3(\text{_____})$

   $y =$ _____

   Solution: (_____, _____)

2. $\begin{cases} 3x + y = 25 \\ y = x - 3 \end{cases}$

   Substitute _____ for y in the first equation.

   $3x + ($ _____ $) = 25$

   _____ $-3 = 25$

   $+3$ $+3$

   _____ $= 28$

   $\div$ _____ $\div$ _____

   _____ $=$ _____

   Since $x =$ _____, substitute _____ for x in one of the equations to find the value of y:

   $y = x - 3$

   $y =$ _____ $- 3$

   $y =$ _____

   Solution: (_____, _____)

Solve each system by substitution. Check your answer.

3. $\begin{cases} y = 4x \\ y = 2x + 6 \end{cases}$

_____

4. $\begin{cases} y = x - 2 \\ 2x + y = 4 \end{cases}$

5. A decorator charges a $45 consultation fee, plus $20 per hour. Another decorator charges a $30 consultation fee, plus $26 per hour.

   a. Write a system of equations to represent the situation.

   _____

   b. Solve the system by substitution. For what number of hours will the total charge be the same? _____

   c. What will that charge be? _____

Holt McDougal Algebra 1

Problem Solving

LESSON 5-2

Solving Systems by Substitution

Write the correct answer.

1. Maribel has $1.25 in her pocket. The money is in quarters and dimes. She has a total of 8 coins. How many quarters and dimes does Maribel have in her pocket?

   Solution:

   $0.25q + 0.10d = 1.25$

   $q + d = 8$

   $q = 8 - d$

   $0.25(8 - d) + 0.10d = 1.25$

   $2 - 0.25d + 0.10d = 1.25$

   $-0.15d = -0.75$

   $d = 5$

   $q = 3$

2. Fabulously Fit offers memberships for $35 per month plus a $50 fee. The Fitness Studio offers memberships for $40 per month plus a $35 fee. In how many months will the fitness clubs cost the same? What will the cost be?

   _____

   _____

Use the chart below to answer questions 3–6. Select the best answer. The chart compares the quotes from four different flooring contractors to tear out and replace a floor.

3. Which expression shows the total cost if the work is done by Dad's Floors?

   A $8 + 150x$ C $150(8x)$

   B $150 + 8x$

4. How many square feet would you need to have installed to make the total cost of V.I.P. Inc. the same as the total cost of Floorshop?

   F 10 ft²   H 100 ft²

   G 200 ft²

5. When the total costs of V.I.P. Inc. and Floorshop are the same, what is the total cost?

   A $1125.00   C $3187.50

   B $1900.00

Contractor	Cost to remove old floor	Cost of new floor per square foot
Smith & Son	$250	$8.00
V.I.P. Inc.	$350	$7.75
Dad's Floors	$150	$8.00
Floorshop	$300	$8.25

6. How many square feet would you need to have installed to make the total cost of Smith & Son the same as the total cost of V.I.P. Inc.?

   F 80 ft²   H 400 ft²

   G 100 ft²

Name _____ Date _____ Class _____

Practice A
Solving Systems by Elimination

Fill in the blanks to solve each system by elimination.

1. $\begin{cases} x + 3y = 14 \\ 2x - 3y = -8 \end{cases}$

Add the equations:

$\quad x + 3y = 14$
$+2x - 3y = -8$
_____

$\quad 3x + \underline{\;0\;} = 6$

$\quad \dfrac{3x}{\quad} = 6$

$\quad \div \underline{\;3\;} \div \underline{\;3\;}$

$\qquad x = \underline{\;2\;}$

Substitute ____ for x in

one of the equations:

$\quad x + 3y = 14$

$\quad \underline{\quad} + 3y = 14$

$\quad - \underline{\quad} \quad - \underline{\quad}$

$\qquad 3y = \underline{\qquad}$

$\qquad \div 3 \;\; \div 3$

$\qquad y = \underline{\quad}$

Solution: (____ , ____)

2. $\begin{cases} 2x + 2y = 4 \\ 3x + 2y = 7 \end{cases}$

Subtract the equations:

$\quad 2x + 2y = 4$
$-(3x + 2y = 7)$
_____

or

$\quad 2x + 2y = 4$

$\quad -3x - \underline{\quad} = \underline{\quad}$

$\quad -x + \underline{\quad} = \underline{\quad}$

$\qquad -x = \underline{\quad}$

$\qquad x = \underline{\quad}$

Substitute ____ for x in

one of the equations:

$\quad 3x + 2y = 7$

$\quad 3(\underline{\quad}) + 2y = 7$

$\qquad \underline{\quad} + 2y = 7$

$\quad - \underline{\quad} \quad - \underline{\quad}$

$\qquad 2y = \underline{\quad}$

$\qquad \div \underline{\quad} \;\; \div \underline{\quad}$

$\qquad y = \underline{\quad}$

Solution: (____ , ____)

3. $\begin{cases} 3x + 4y = 26 \\ x - 2y = -8 \end{cases}$

Multiply the second equation by 2. Then, add the equations:

$\begin{cases} 3x + 4y = 26 \\ 2(x - 2y = -8) \end{cases}$

$\quad 3x + 4y = 26$

$\quad + \underline{\quad} x - \underline{\quad} y = \underline{\quad}$

$\qquad \underline{\quad} x + 0 = \underline{\quad}$

$\qquad \underline{\quad} x = \underline{\quad}$

Substitute ____ for x in

one of the equations:

$\quad x - 2y = -8$

$\quad \underline{\quad} - 2y = -8$

$\qquad -2y = \underline{\quad}$

$\qquad \div \underline{\quad} \;\; \div \underline{\quad}$

$\qquad y = \underline{\quad}$

Solution: (____ , ____)

Solve each system by elimination.

4. $\begin{cases} 3x - 2y = 1 \\ 2x + 2y = 14 \end{cases}$

5. $\begin{cases} x + y = 4 \\ 3x + y = 16 \end{cases}$

6. $\begin{cases} 3x + 2y = -26 \\ 2x - 6y = -10 \end{cases}$

_____   _____   _____

Holt McDougal Algebra 1

Problem Solving

Solving Systems by Elimination

Write the correct answer.

1. The Lees spent $31 on movie tickets for 2 adults and 3 children. The Macias spent $26 on movie tickets for 2 adults and 2 children. What are the prices for adult and child movie tickets?

   Solution:

   $2a + 3c = 31$

   $2a + 2c = 26$

   $c = 5$

   $a = 8$

2. Last month Stephanie spent $57 on 4 allergy shots and 1 office visit. This month she spent $9 after 1 office visit and a refund for 2 allergy shots from her insurance company. How much does an office visit cost? an allergy shot?

   $4a + v =$ _____

   $-2a + v =$ _____

   _____

Use the chart below to answer questions 3–4. Select the best answer. The chart shows the price per pound for dried fruit.

Dried Fruit Price List			
Pineapple	Apple	Mango	Papaya
$7.50/lb	$7.00/lb	$8.00/lb	$7.25/lb

3. Suki bought 5 pounds of mango and papaya for $37.75. How many pounds of each fruit did Suki buy?

   A 2 lb mango and 3 lb papaya

   B 3 lb mango and 2 lb papaya

   C 1 lb mango and 4 lb papaya

4. Two gift baskets of dried fruit each cost $100.

   First basket: 12 lb fruit *x*

   2 lb fruit *y*

   Second basket: 4 lb fruit *x*

   9 lb fruit *y*

   Which two fruits were used in the baskets?

   F pineapple and apple

   G apple and mango

   H mango and papaya

LESSON 5-4 Practice A

Solving Special Systems

Solve each system of linear equations. Tell whether the system has no solution or infinitely many solutions. The first one is done for you.

1. $\begin{cases} 2x + y = 1 \\ 2x + y = -3 \end{cases}$

2. $\begin{cases} y = 5x + 2 \\ y - 5x = 2 \end{cases}$

$$\text{Since } 1 \neq 3, \text{ there is}$$

$$\text{no solution}$$

3. $\begin{cases} y - 3x + 2 = 0 \\ 2 = -y + 3x \end{cases}$

4. $\begin{cases} x + y = 4 \\ y - 4 = 1 - x \end{cases}$

Give the number of solutions to each system. Then classify the system as "consistent, independent", "consistent, dependent", or "inconsistent".

5. $\begin{cases} y = 2(x + 1) \\ y - 2x = 2 \end{cases}$

6. $\begin{cases} y - 4x + 5 = 0 \\ 4x = y - 1 \end{cases}$

> **consistent, independent:** exactly one solution
> **consistent, dependent:** infinitely many solutions
> **inconsistent:** no solutions

7. Mark opens a savings account with $60 and adds $20 each month. His brother Jibran adds $20 each month to his savings account that he opened with $60. If the brothers continue to make deposits to their savings accounts at the same rate, when will they have the same amount of money? Explain.

_____

_____

LESSON 5-4

Problem Solving
Solving Special Systems

Write the correct answer.

1. Tyra has biked 256 miles so far and rides 48 miles per week. Charmian has biked 125 miles so far and rides 48 miles per week. If these rates continue, will Tyra's distance ever equal Charmian's distance? Explain.

   Solution:

   No, the graphs are parallel lines.

2. Metroplexpress charges $15 to pick up a package and $0.50 per mile. Local Express charges $10 to pick up a package and $0.55 per mile. Classify this system. Find its solution, if any.

   consistent, independent

   _____

3. The Singhs start savings accounts for their twin boys. The accounts earn 5% annual interest. The initial deposit in each account is $200. Classify this system. Find its solution, if any.

   _____

   _____

Select the best answer.

4. An apartment at The Oaks costs $400 per month plus a $350 deposit. An apartment at Crossroads costs $400 per month plus a $300 deposit. How many solutions does this system have?

   A no solutions

   B 1 solution

   C an infinite number of solutions

6. A tank filled with 75 liters of water loses 0.5 liter of water per hour. A tank filled with 50 liters of water loses 0.1 liter of water per hour. How would this system be classified?

   A inconsistent

   B consistent and independent

   C consistent and dependent

5. Simon is 3 years older than Renata. Five years ago, Renata was half as old as Simon is now. How old are Simon and Renata now?

   F Simon is 13 and Renata is 10.

   G Simon is 16 and Renata is 8.

   H Simon is 16 and Renata is 13.

Holt McDougal Algebra 1

LESSON | **Practice A**
5-5

Solving Linear Inequalities

Use substitution to tell whether the ordered pair is a solution of the given inequality. The first one is done for you.

1. $(3, 4); y > x + 2$ 2. $(4, 2); y \le 2x - 3$ 3. $(2, -1); y < -x$

        4 > 3 + 2, no _____   _____   _____

Rewrite each linear inequality in slope-intercept form. Then graph the solutions in the coordinate plane. The first one is started for you.

4. $y - x \le 3$

     $y \le 3 + x$

5. $6x + 2y > -2$

     _____

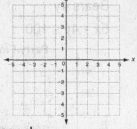

6. Trey is choosing yogurt at the grocery store. The flavors he likes are peach x and blueberry y. His mother said he may choose at most 8 containers of yogurt.

    a. Write an inequality to describe the situation.

      _____

    b. Graph the solutions.

    c. Give two possible combinations of peach and blueberry yogurt that Trey can choose.

      _____

      _____

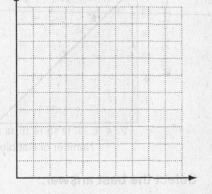

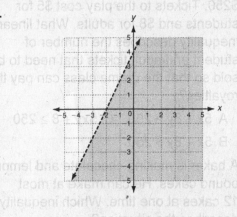

Write an inequality to represent each graph.

7.

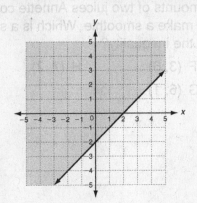

     _____

8.

     _____

       Holt McDougal Algebra 1

LESSON
5-5
Problem Solving
Solving Linear Inequalities

Write the correct answer.

1. Shania would like to give $5 rabbits and $4 teddy bears as party favors. Shania has $100 to spend on party favors. Write and graph an inequality to find the number of rabbits x and teddy bears y Shania could purchase.

   Solution:

   Rabbits $5x$

   Bears $4y$

   $5x + 4y \le 100$

   $25 \times 4 = 100$

   $20 \times 5 = 100$

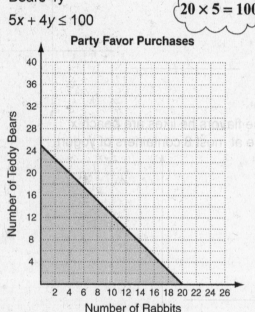

   Party Favor Purchases

2. Hank has 20 yards of lumber to build a raised garden. Write and graph a linear inequality for the possible lengths and widths of the garden.

   $2x + 2y \le 20$

   $p = 2l + 2w$

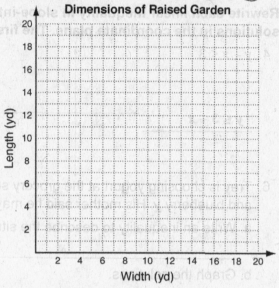

   Dimensions of Raised Garden

Select the best answer.

3. The costs for the high school play are $250. Tickets to the play cost $5 for students and $8 for adults. What linear inequality describes the number of student and adult tickets that need to be sold so that the drama class can pay the royalties?

   A $5x + 8y \ge 250$ C $5xy + 8 \ge 250$

   B $5x + 8y > 250$

4. The inequality $x + y \le 8$ describes the amounts of two juices Annette combines to make a smoothie. Which is a solution to the inequality?

   F (3, 6)   H (7, 2)

   G (6, 1)

5. A baker is making chocolate and lemon pound cakes. He can make at most 12 cakes at one time. Which inequality describes the situation?

   A $x + y \ge 12$ C $x + y < 12$

   B $x + y \le 12$

Holt McDougal Algebra 1

**LESSON
5-6**

Practice A

Solving Systems of Linear Inequalities

**Tell whether the ordered pair is a solution of the given system.
The first one is done for you.**

1. $(4, 5); \begin{cases} y \le x + 2 \\ y \ge x - 1 \end{cases}$

2. $(1, 3); \begin{cases} y > 3x \\ y < x + 2 \end{cases}$

3. $(2, 3); \begin{cases} y < 5x - 3 \\ y \ge -x \end{cases}$

   $5 \le 4 + 2, 5 \ge 4 - 1, \text{ yes}$ _____

**Graph the system of linear inequalities. a. Give two ordered pairs that are solutions.
b. Give two ordered pairs that are not solutions. The first one is started for you**

4. $\begin{cases} y \ge x + 1 \\ y \le -2x \end{cases}$

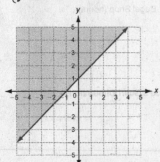

5. $\begin{cases} y < 2x + 4 \\ y > x - 1 \end{cases}$

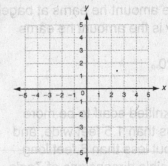

a. ___**(−1,0) and (−3,2)**___

a. _____

b. ___**(0,−3) and (4,0)**___

b. _____

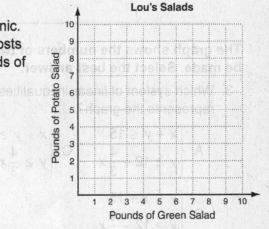

Lou's Salads

6. Lou is buying green salad and potato salad for a picnic.
   Green salad costs $4 per pound and potato salad costs
   $2 per pound. Lou would like to buy at least 6 pounds of
   salads and wants to spend no more than $20.

   a. Write a system of linear inequalities.
      Let x = pounds of green salad
      Let y = pounds of potato salad

   _____

   b. Graph the solutions of the system.

   c. Describe all the possible combinations of pounds of salads that Lou could buy.

   _____

   _____

   d. List two possible combinations. _____

   _____

Holt McDougal Algebra 1

LESSON 5-6 **Problem Solving**

Solving Systems of Linear Inequalities

Write the correct answer.

1. Paul earns $7 per hour at the bagel shop and $12 per hour mowing lawns. Paul needs to earn at least $120 per week, but he must work less than 30 hours per week. Write and graph the system of linear inequalities that describes this situation.

Solution:

Let x be hours at bagel shop.
Let y be hours mowing.
Then $7x$ is the amount he earns at bagel shop and $12y$ is the amount he earns mowing.

$7x + 12y \geq 120$
$x + y < 30$

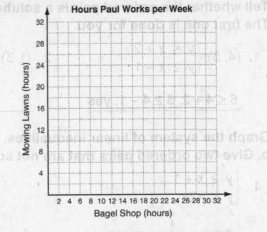

Hours Paul Works per Week

Bagel Shop (hours)

2. Zoe wants a knitted scarf to be more than 1 but less than 1.5 feet wide, and more than 6 but less than 8 feet long. Graph all possible dimensions of Zoe's scarf. List two possible combinations.

_____

_____

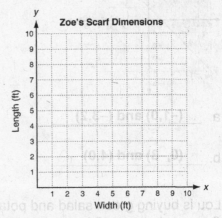

Zoe's Scarf Dimensions

Length (ft)

Width (ft)

The graph shows the numbers of two types of wood tables that can be made. Select the best answer.

3. Which system of linear inequalities represents the graph?

A $\begin{cases} x + y \leq 15 \\ y \geq 12 - \dfrac{4}{3}x \end{cases}$ C $\begin{cases} x + y \geq 15 \\ y \geq \dfrac{4}{3}x - 12 \end{cases}$

B $\begin{cases} y \leq x + 15 \\ y \geq 12 - \dfrac{4}{3}x \end{cases}$

4. If 6 buffet tables are built, which can NOT be the number of dining tables built?

  F 4   H 10

  G 6

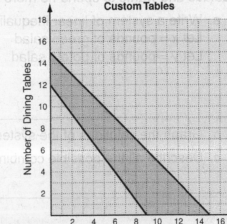

Custom Tables

Number of Dining Tables

Number of Buffet Tables

Holt McDougal Algebra 1

CHAPTER
5

Systems of Equations and Inequalities

Section A Quiz

Select the best answer.

1. Which ordered pair is the solution of the system graphed below?

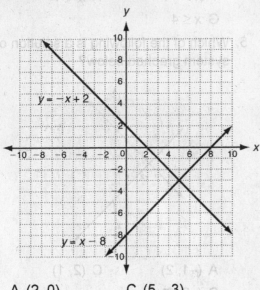

$y = -x + 2$

$y = x - 8$

   A (2, 0)   C (5, −3)

   B (−3, 5)

2. What does it mean if (3, 2) is a solution of $\begin{cases} y = x - 1 \\ y = -x + 5 \end{cases}$?

   F (3, 2) makes at least one of the equations true.

   G (3, 2) makes both equations true.

   H (3, 2) makes neither equation true.

3. Solve $\begin{cases} y = x + 3 \\ 2x + y = -6 \end{cases}$ by substitution.

   A (−9, −6)   C (−1, 2)

   B (−3, 0)

4. Solve $\begin{cases} y = 4x - 1 \\ y = 3x + 6 \end{cases}$ by substitution.

   F (7, 29)   H (7, 27)

   G (1, 3)

5. Solve $\begin{cases} y = 2x \\ y = 4x + 12 \end{cases}$ by substitution.

   A (4, 8)   C (−6, −12)

   B (−4, −8)

6. Solve $\begin{cases} x + y = -1 \\ x - y = -7 \end{cases}$ by elimination.

   F (−4, 3)   H (3, −4)

   G (−3, 2)

7. Solve $\begin{cases} 2x - 3y = -14 \\ 3x + 3y = 9 \end{cases}$ by elimination.

   A (1, 2)   C (1, −4)

   B (−1, 4)

8. Joe spent $7.75 to purchase 23 snacks. Chips are $0.25 and pretzels are $0.50. How many of each type of snack did Joe buy?

   F 8 bags of chips; 15 bags of pretzels

   G 15 bags of chips; 8 bags of pretzels

   H 11 bags of chips; 12 bags of pretzels

9. Which is true about the equations of a linear system if the system is classified as inconsistent?

   A Their slopes are the same, but their *y*-intercepts are different.

   B Their slopes are different, but their *y*-intercepts are the same.

   C Their slopes are different, and their *y*-intercepts are different.

10. How many solutions does the system $\begin{cases} y = 2x + 1 \\ -4x + 2y = 2 \end{cases}$ have?

   F none   H infinitely many

   G exactly two

Holt McDougal Algebra 1

CHAPTER 5 Systems of Equations and Inequalities

Section B Quiz

Select the best answer.

1. Which inequality is represented by the graph shown?

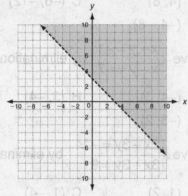

A $y \geq -x + 3$ C $y > -x + 3$

B $y < -x + 3$

2. Which ordered pair is a solution of the system graphed below?

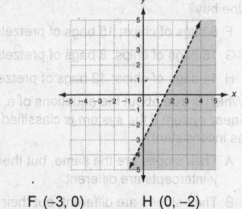

F (–3, 0)   H (0, –2)

G (3, 2)

3. Which is the graph of $y \geq -2x + 1$?

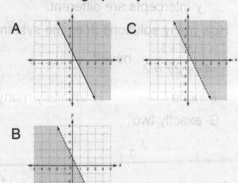

4. For which would you draw a dashed boundary line and shade to the left?

F $x > -4$ H $x < 4$

G $x \leq 4$

5. Which of the following is a solution of the system graphed below?

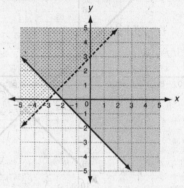

A (–1, 2)   C (2, 1)

B (–3, 3)

6. Which is true for $\begin{cases} y > x + 1 \\ y > x + 3 \end{cases}$?

F The solutions are the points between the two lines.

G The solutions are the same as the solutions of $y > x + 1$.

H The solutions are the same as the solutions of $y > x + 3$.

7. The drama club is having a car wash. They wash x cars at $5 each and y trucks at $8 each. They will wash at least 26 cars and 15 trucks. They need to make at least $250. Which system describes this situation?

A $\begin{cases} x \geq 26 \\ y \geq 15 \\ 5x + 8y \leq 250 \end{cases}$ C $\begin{cases} x \geq 26 \\ y \geq 15 \\ 5x + 8y \geq 250 \end{cases}$

B $\begin{cases} x > 26 \\ y > 15 \\ 5x + 8y > 250 \end{cases}$

Holt McDougal Algebra 1

CHAPTER
5

Systems of Equations and Inequalities
Chapter Test Form A

Select the best answer.

1. Which ordered pair is a solution of
$\begin{cases} x = 2y + 1 \\ y = x \end{cases}$?

   A (−1, −1)

   B (3, 1)

2. The graph of a system of linear equations is shown below. What is the solution of the system?

   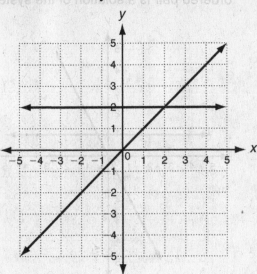

   A (0, 0)

   B (2, 2)

   C (0, 2)

3. Solve by substitution: $\begin{cases} y = x + 1 \\ x + y = 7 \end{cases}$.

   A (0, 1)   C (3, 4)

   B (6, 7)

4. Solve by elimination: $\begin{cases} 2x + y = 10 \\ x + y = 2 \end{cases}$.

   A (4, −2)

   B (8, −6)

5. Leslie joins a fitness club that has a membership fee of $20 plus $15 per month. Rashad's club has a fee of $40 and charges $10 per month. In how many months will the two clubs cost the same?

   A 4 months

   B 12 months

6. Solve by any method: $\begin{cases} -x + y = 1 \\ x + y = 3 \end{cases}$.

   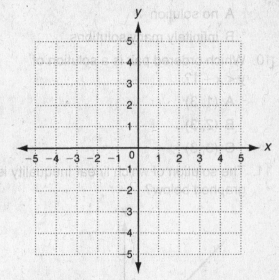

   A (2, 1)

   B (1, 2)

7. Which term describes a system with exactly one solution?

   A consistent and independent

   B consistent and dependent

   C inconsistent

**CHAPTER
5**

Systems of Equations and Inequalities

Chapter Test Form A continued

8. Which equation would make this system have an infinite number of solutions?

$$\begin{cases} y = x + 2 \\ \underline{} \end{cases}$$

A $2y = 2x + 2$

B $y - 2 = x$

C $y = 2x$

9. Solve $\begin{cases} x = 2y + 4 \\ 2y = x - 6 \end{cases}$

A no solution

B infinitely many solutions

10. Which ordered pair is a solution of $y < x + 1$?

A $(1, 3)$

B $(2, 3)$

C $(3, 3)$

11. The solution of which linear inequality is graphed below?

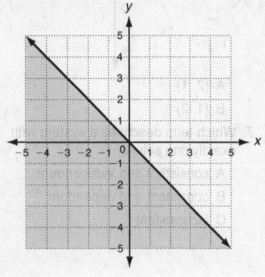

A $y < -x$ C $y \leq -x$

B $y > -x$

12. For which system of linear inequalities is the ordered pair $(1, -1)$ a solution?

A $\begin{cases} y \leq -x + 1 \\ y > x + 1 \end{cases}$

B $\begin{cases} y \leq x - 1 \\ y > x - 3 \end{cases}$

13. The graph of a system of linear inequalities is shown below. Which ordered pair is a solution of the system?

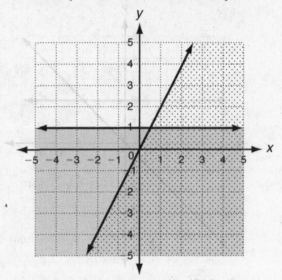

A $(-2, 2)$ C $(2, -2)$

B $(4, 3)$

14. Amber is buying drinks and snacks. She can spend no more than $20. Drinks d cost $1 each. Snacks s cost $2 each. She needs at least 5 of each snack. What system represents this situation?

A $\begin{cases} d > 5 \\ s > 5 \\ d + s \leq 20 \end{cases}$

B $\begin{cases} d \geq 5 \\ s \geq 5 \\ d + 2s \leq 20 \end{cases}$

Holt McDougal Algebra 1

LESSON 6-1

Practice A

Integer Exponents

Simplify. The first one has been done for you.

1. $3^{-2} = \dfrac{1}{3^2} = \dfrac{1}{\underline{3} \cdot \underline{3}} = \dfrac{1}{\underline{9}}$

2. $2^{-4} = \dfrac{1}{2^4} = \dfrac{1}{\underline{} \cdot \underline{} \cdot \underline{} \cdot \underline{}} = \dfrac{1}{\underline{}}$

3. $(-3)^{-3} = \dfrac{1}{(\underline{})^3} = \dfrac{1}{\underline{} \cdot \underline{} \cdot \underline{}} = \dfrac{1}{\underline{}}$

4. $(-1)^{-5} = \dfrac{1}{(\underline{})^5} = \dfrac{1}{\underline{} \cdot \underline{} \cdot \underline{} \cdot \underline{} \cdot \underline{}} = \dfrac{1}{\underline{}} = \underline{}$

5. $-(7.2)^0$ _____

6. $(4)^{-3}$ _____

Evaluate each expression for the given value(s) of the variable(s).

> **evaluate:**
> find the value of

7. x^{-2} for $x = 3$

$(3)^{-2} = \dfrac{1}{(\underline{\,3\,})^2} = \dfrac{1}{\underline{}}$

8. $m^0 n^{-3}$ for $m = 2$ and $n = 3$

$(\underline{})^0 (\underline{})^{-3} = (\underline{}) \cdot \dfrac{1}{(\underline{})^3}$

9. $5r^{-4}$ for $r = -2$

$5(\underline{})^{-4} = 5 \cdot \dfrac{1}{(\underline{})^-}$

$= 5 \cdot \dfrac{1}{\underline{} \cdot \underline{} \cdot \underline{} \cdot \underline{}}$

$= 5 \cdot \dfrac{1}{\underline{}} = \dfrac{}{}$

Simplify.

10. $4x^{-3}$

_____

11. $\dfrac{5}{b^{-2}}$

_____

12. $\dfrac{k^{-4}}{2}$

_____

13. $\dfrac{f^4}{g^{-1}}$

_____

14. The weight of a silver charm is 2^{-2} grams. Evaluate this expression.

_____

LESSON 6-1

Problem Solving

Integer Exponents

Write the correct answer.

1. The mu-chip was developed in 2003. Its area is $4^2(10)^{-2}$ square millimeters. Simplify this expression.

   Solution:

   $$4^2(10)^{-2} = \frac{4^2}{10^2}$$

   $$= \frac{16}{100} = \frac{4}{25} \text{ or } 0.16$$

   _____ **0.16 mm²**

2. An adult Northern Yellow Bat has a wingspan of about 14 inches and weighs between $3(2)^{-3}$ and $3(2)^{-2}$ ounces. Simplify these expressions.

   _____

   _____

3. The volume of a tank can be expressed in terms of x, y, and z. Expressed in these terms, the volume of the tank is $x^3 y^{-2} z$ liters. Determine the volume of the tank if $x = 4$, $y = 3$, and $z = 6$.

   _____

The masses of four insects are shown in the table below. Select the best answer.

Insect	Mass
Emperor Scorpion	2^{-5} kg
African Goliath Beetle	11^{-1} kg
Giant Weta	2^{-4} kg
Madagascar Hissing Cockroach	5^{-3} kg

4. What is the mass of the Madagascar Hissing Cockroach expressed as a quotient?

   A $-\dfrac{1}{125}$ kg   C $\dfrac{1}{15}$ kg

   B $\dfrac{1}{125}$ kg

5. Which expression is another way to show the mass of the Giant Weta?

   F $-(2)^4$ kg   H $\dfrac{1}{2 \cdot 2 \cdot 2 \cdot 2}$ kg

   G $\left(\dfrac{1}{2}\right)^{-4}$ kg

6. What is the mass of the Emperor Scorpion expressed as a quotient?

   A $-\dfrac{1}{32}$ kg   C $\dfrac{1}{32}$ kg

   B $\dfrac{1}{25}$ kg

LESSON 6-2

Practice A

Rational Exponents

Match each expression with a fractional exponent to an equivalent radical expression. Write the correct letter on the answer blank. The first one is done for you.

1. $x^{\frac{1}{2}}$ _____ **B** _____   A. $\left(\sqrt{x}\right)^3$

2. $x^{\frac{1}{3}}$ _____   B. $\sqrt{x}$

3. $x^{\frac{2}{3}}$ _____   C. $\left(\sqrt[3]{x}\right)^2$

4. $x^{\frac{3}{2}}$ _____   D. $\sqrt[3]{x}$

Simplify each expression. All variables represent nonnegative numbers. The first one is done for you.

5. $49^{\frac{1}{2}}$ 6. $81^{\frac{1}{4}}$ 7. $1^{\frac{1}{3}}$

       7

8. $8^{\frac{1}{3}} + 100^{\frac{1}{2}}$ 9. $16^{\frac{3}{4}}$ 10. $27^{\frac{2}{3}}$

11. $1^{\frac{2}{5}}$ 12. $8^{\frac{5}{3}}$ 13. $\sqrt{x^{16}}$

14. Given a square with area x, you can use the formula $d = 1.4x^{\frac{1}{2}}$ to estimate the length of the diagonal of the square. Use the formula to estimate the length of the diagonal of a square with area 100 cm^2 (*Hint:* $x = 100$)

_____

LESSON 6-2 Problem Solving
Rational Exponents

Write the correct answer.

1. For a pendulum with a length of L meters, the time in seconds that it takes the pendulum to swing back and forth is approximately $2L^{\frac{1}{2}}$. About how long does it take a pendulum that is 9 meters long to swing back and forth?

Solution:

$2L^{\frac{1}{2}}$ for $L = 9$

$2(9)^{\frac{1}{2}}$

$2\left(\sqrt{9}\right)$

$2(3)$

It takes 6 seconds.

_____

2. The Beaufort Scale is used to measure the intensity of tornados. For a tornado with Beaufort number B, the formula $v = 1.9B^{\frac{3}{2}}$ may be used to estimate the tornado's wind speed in miles per hour. Estimate the wind speed of a tornado with Beaufort number 9.

$v = 1.9B^{\frac{3}{2}}$

$v = 1.9(9)^{\frac{3}{2}}$

$v = 1.9\sqrt{\boxed{}}^{3}$

$v = 1.9(\underline{})$

$v = \underline{}$

The estimated speed of wind is _____ mi/h.

Given an animal's body mass m, in grams, the formula $B = 1.8m^{\frac{3}{4}}$ may be used to estimate the mass B, in grams, of the animal's brain. The table shows the body mass of several birds. Use the table for questions 3–4. Select the best answer.

3. Which is the best estimate for the brain mass of a macaw?

  A 9 g   C 225 g

  B 45 g

5. An animal has a body mass given by the expression x^4. Which expression can be used to estimate the animal's brain mass?

  A $B = 1.8x^3$ C $B = 1.8x^{12}$

  B $B = 1.8x^{\frac{3}{4}}$

4. How much larger is the brain mass of a barn owl compared to the brain mass of a cockatiel?

  F 189 g   H 388.8 g

  G 340.2 g

Typical Body Masses of Birds	
Bird	Body Mass (g)
Cockatiel	81
Guam Rail	256
Macaw	625
Barn Owl	1296

Sources:

http://www.beyondveg.com/billings-t/comp-anat/comp-anat-appx2.shtml

http://www.sandiegozoo.org/animalbytes/index.html

LESSON 6-3

Practice A

Polynomials

Find the degree and number of terms of each polynomial.
The first one is done for you.

1. $4w^2$

2. $9x^3 + 2x$

3. $4p^5 - p^3 + p^2 + 11$

Degree: ____2____

Degree: _____

Degree: _____

Terms: ____1____

Terms: _____

Terms: _____

Fill in each blank with _monomial_, _binomial_, or _trinomial_.

4. A _____ is a polynomial with three terms.

5. A _____ is a polynomial with one term.

6. A _____ is a polynomial with two terms.

> **standard form:**
> degrees in order,
> highest first
> **leading coefficient:**
> coefficient of first
> term in standard form

Write each polynomial in standard form.
Then, give the leading coefficient.

7. $12 + 3x^2 - x$ _____

8. $g^4 - 2g^3 - g^5$ _____

9. $k^2 + k^4 - k^3 + 1$ _____

First, classify each polynomial by its degree (_linear_, _quadratic_, _cubic_, or _quartic_).
Then, classify it by its number of terms (_monomial_, _binomial_, or _trinomial_).

10. $109z^2$

11. $3x + 11$

12. $b^3 - 2 + 2b^4$

_____

_____

_____

13. Complete the table by evaluating the polynomial for each value of z.

Polynomial	$z = 0$	$z = 1$	$z = 2$	$z = -1$
$2z + 3z^2 - 3$				

14. The surface area of a cylinder is approximated by the
polynomial $6r^2 + 6rh$, where r is the radius and
h is the height of the cylinder. Find the approximate
surface area of the cylinder at right.

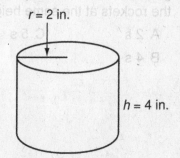

$r = 2$ in.

$h = 4$ in.

_____

Holt McDougal Algebra 1

LESSON 6-3 Problem Solving

Polynomials

Write the correct answer.

1. The surface area of a cylinder is given by the polynomial $2\pi r^2 + 2\pi rh$. A cylinder has a radius of 2 centimeters and a height of 5 centimeters. Find its surface area. Use 3.14 for π.

   Solution:

   S.A. $= 2\pi r^2 + 2\pi rh$

   $r = 2,\ h = 5$

   S.A. $= 2 \cdot 3.14 \cdot 2^2 + 2 \cdot 3.14 \cdot 2 \cdot 5$

   $= 6.28 \cdot 4 + 6.28 \cdot 10$

   $= 87.92$

   $= 87.92\ \text{cm}^2$

2. A firework is launched from the ground at a velocity of 180 feet per second. Its height after t seconds is given by the polynomial $-16t^2 + 180t$. Find the height of the firework after 2 seconds and after 5 seconds.

   $h = -16(2)^2 + 180 \cdot 2$

   _____

   _____

3. The volume of a box is given by $4h^3 - 10h^2 + 6h$. Find the volume of the box for $h = 0.25$ and $h = 0.5$.

   _____

   _____

The height of a rocket in meters t seconds after it is launched is approximated by the polynomial $0.5at^2 + vt + h$ where a is always -9.8, v is the initial velocity, and h is the initial height. Use this information with the data in the chart for questions 4–5. Select the best answer.

4. A 300X rocket was launched from a height of 10 meters. What was its height after 3 seconds?

   A 715.9 m   C 755.5 m

   B 745.3 m

Model Number	Initial Velocity (m/s)
300X	250
Q99	90
4400i	125

5. The 4400i rocket was launched from the ground at the same time the Q99 rocket was launched from 175 meters above the ground. After how many seconds were the rockets at the same height?

   A 2 s   C 5 s

   B 4 s

    Holt McDougal Algebra 1

LESSON 6-4

Practice A

Adding and Subtracting Polynomials

Add or subtract. The first one is done for you.

1. $3x^3 + 4 + x^3 - 10$ _____ $(3x^3 + x^3) + (4 - 10) = 4x^3 - 6$

2. $6 - 12p^5 - 3p + 8 - 8p^5$ _____

Add.

3. $2m + 4$
   $+ m + 2$
   _____

4. $3y^2 - y + 3$
   $+ 2y^2 + 2y + 9$
   _____

5. $4z^3 + 3z^2 + 8$
   $+ 2z^3 + z^2 - 3$
   _____

6. $(10g^2 + 3g - 10) + (2g^2 + g + 9)$ _____

Subtract.

7. $12k + 3$
   $- (4k + 2)$
   _____

8. $6s^3 + 9s + 10$
   $- (3s^3 + 4s - 10)$
   _____

9. $15a^4 + 6a^2 + a$
   $- (6a^4 - 2a^2 + a)$
   _____

10. $(11b^2 + 3b - 1) - (2b^2 + 2b + 8)$ _____

11. Write a polynomial that represents the difference between the
    measures of angle GEO and angle OEM.
    (Hint: $\angle GEO = (3w + 7)°$
    $\angle OEM = (2w - 1)°$)

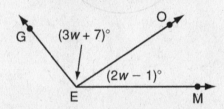

12. Becki is building a pen for her rabbits against the side of
    her house.

    a. Find the difference between the length
       and the width of the pen.

    _____

    b. Find the perimeter of the pen NOT including
       the side of the house.

    _____

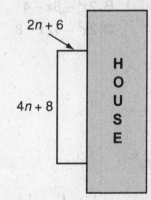

Holt McDougal Algebra 1

LESSON 6-4
Problem Solving
Adding and Subtracting Polynomials

Write the correct answer.

1. The volume of one box is $4x^3 + 4x^2$ cubic units. The volume of the second box is $6x^3 - 18x^2$ cubic units. Write a polynomial for the total volume of the two boxes.

Solution:

First box: $4x^3 + 4x^2$

Second box: $6x^3 - 18x^2$

Total: $10x^3 - 14x^2$

$10x^3 - 14x^2$ cubic units

2. A recreation field is shaped like a rectangle with a length of $15x$ yards and a width of $10x - 3$ yards. Write a polynomial for the perimeter of the field. Then calculate the perimeter if $x = 2$. (*Hint: $P = 2l + 2w$*)

_____

_____

The circle graph represents election results for the president of the math team. Use the graph for questions 3–4. Select the best answer.

3. The angle value of Greg's sector is $x^2 + 6x + 2$. The angle value of Dion's sector is $7x + 20$. Which polynomial represents both sectors combined?

  A $x^2 + x + 18$

  B $x^2 + 13x + 22$

  C $7x^2 + 6x + 22$

Math Team Election Results

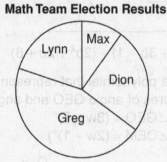

4. The sum of Lynn's sector and Max's sector is $2x^2 - 9x - 2$. Max's sector is $3x + 6$. Which polynomial represents Lynn's sector?

  A $2x^2 - 6x + 4$

  B $2x^2 - 6x - 4$

  C $2x^2 - 12x - 8$

LESSON 6-5	**Practice A**
	Multiplying Polynomials

Multiply. The first one is done for you.

1. $(4x)(5x)$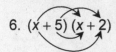

$20x^2$

2. $(3x^2)(5x)$

3. $(6y^2)(3y^3)$

4. $3(5x + 7)$

_____

5. $4x(2x^2 + 7x + 3)$

_____

Fill in the blanks by multiplying the First, Outer, Inner, and Last terms. Then simplify. The first one is started for you.

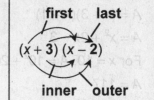

6. $(x + 5)(x + 2)$

7. $(x + 4)(x - 3)$

x^2	$2x$	$5x$	10
F	O	I	L

Simplify: _____

Simplify: _____

Fill in the blanks below. Then simplify.

8. $(x + 3)(x^2 + 4x + 7) = x(x^2 + 4x + 7) + 3(x^2 + 4x + 7)$

Distribute: _____ _____ _____ + _____ _____ _____

Simplify: _____

9. The length of a rectangle is 5 inches greater than the width.

 a. Write an expression for the width of the rectangle. _____

 b. Write an expression for the length of the rectangle. _____

 c. Write a simplified expression for the area of the rectangle.
 (Area = length × width) _____

 d. Find the area of the rectangle when the width is
 3 inches. _____

 e. Find the area of the rectangle when the length is
 9 inches. _____

Holt McDougal Algebra 1

Name _____ Date _____ Class_____

LESSON **Problem Solving**
6-5
Multiplying Polynomials

Write the correct answer.

1. A bedroom has a length of $x + 3$ feet and a width of $x - 1$ feet. Write a polynomial to express the area of the bedroom. Then calculate the area if $x = 10$.

   Solution:

   $A = l \cdot w$

   $A = (x + 3)(x - 1)$

   $A = x^2 + 2x - 3$

   For $x = 10$, $A = 10^2 + 20 - 3$

   $A = 117$

   $A = 117 \text{ ft}^2$

2. The length of a classroom is 4 feet longer than its width. Write a polynomial to express the area of the classroom. Then calculate the area if the width is 22 feet. (*Hint: l = w + 4*)

   _____

   _____

   _____

The volume of a pyramid is $\frac{1}{3}Bh$ where B is the area of the base and h is the height of the pyramid. The Great Pyramid of Giza has a square base. Each side is about 300 feet longer than the height of the pyramid. Select the best answer.

3. Which polynomial represents the approximate area of the base of the Great Pyramid?

   A $h^2 + 90,000$

   B $2h + 90,000$

   C $h^2 + 600h + 90,000$

4. Which polynomial represents the approximate volume of the Great Pyramid?

   F $\frac{1}{3}h^3 + 200h^2 + 30,000h$

   G $\frac{1}{3}h^2 + 200h + 30,000$

   H $h^3 + 600h^2 + 90,000h$

Holt McDougal Algebra 1

LESSON 6-6

Practice A
Special Products of Binomials

Fill in the blanks below. Then simplify. The first one is done for you.

1. $(x+5)^2$

$\boxed{x}^2 + 2\left(\boxed{5}\right)\left(\boxed{x}\right) + \boxed{5}^2$

$\underline{x^2 + 10x + 25}$

2. $(m+3)^2$

$\boxed{}^2 + 2\left(\boxed{}\right)\left(\boxed{}\right) + \boxed{}^2$

3. $(2+a)^2$

$\boxed{}^2 + 2\left(\boxed{}\right)\left(\boxed{}\right) + \boxed{}^2$

Multiply.

4. $(x+4)^2$

5. $(a+7)^2$

6. $(8+b)^2$

Fill in the blanks below. Then simplify. The first one is done for you.

7. $(x-10)^2$

$\boxed{x}^2 - 2\left(\boxed{10}\right)\left(\boxed{x}\right) + \boxed{10}^2$

$\underline{x^2 - 20x + 100}$

8. $(y-6)^2$

$\boxed{}^2 - 2\left(\boxed{}\right)\left(\boxed{}\right) + \boxed{}^2$

9. $(9-x)^2$

$\boxed{}^2 - 2\left(\boxed{}\right)\left(\boxed{}\right) + \boxed{}^2$

Multiply.

10. $(y-7)^2$

11. $(b-11)^2$

12. $(3-x)^2$

Fill in the blanks below. Then simplify. The first one is done for you.

13. $(x+7)(x-7)$

$\boxed{x}^2 - \boxed{7}^2$

$\underline{x^2 - 49}$

14. $(4+y)(4-y)$

$\boxed{}^2 - \boxed{}^2$

15. $(x+2)(x-2)$

$\boxed{}^2 - \boxed{}^2$

Multiply.

16. $(x+8)(x-8)$

17. $(3+y)(3-y)$

18. $(x+1)(x-1)$

Holt McDougal Algebra 1

Name _____ Date _____ Class_____

Problem Solving
Special Products of Binomials

Write the correct answer.

1. This week Kyara worked $x + 4$ hours. She is paid $x - 4$ dollars per hour. Write a polynomial for the amount that Kyara earned this week. Then calculate her pay if $x = 12$.

   Solution:

   Pay = hours worked • dollars per hour

   $$= (x + 4)(x - 4)$$
   $$= x^2 - 16$$

   For $x = 12$,

   $$x^2 - 16 = 144 - 16$$
   $$= 128$$

   Pay is $128.

2. A museum set aside part of a large gallery for a special exhibit.

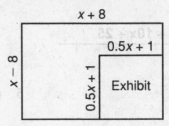

   Write a polynomial for the area of the gallery that is not part of the exhibit. Then calculate the area of that section if $x = 60$. (*Hint:* Find area of gallery minus area of exhibit.)

   _____

   _____

A circle is in the center of a square. The radius of the circle is $x - 2$ feet. The length of the square is $2x + 4$ feet. Use this information and the diagram for questions 3–5. Select the best answer.

3. Which polynomial represents the area of the circle?

   A $\pi x^2 - 4\pi x - 4\pi$

   B $\pi x^2 - 4\pi$

   C $\pi x^2 - 4\pi x + 4\pi$

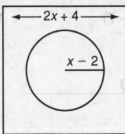

4. Which polynomial represents the area of the square, including the circle?

   F $4x^2 + 8$

   G $4x^2 + 16x + 16$

   H $4x^2 + 8x + 16$

5. Which polynomial represents the area of the garden *outside* the circle? (Use 3.14 for π.)

   A $0.86x^2 + 28.56x + 3.44$

   B $0.86x^2 + 3.44x + 28.56$

   C $7.14x^2 + 28.56x + 3.44$

Holt McDougal Algebra 1

CHAPTER
6

Exponents and Polynomials
Section A Quiz

Select the best answer.

1. Simplify 9^{-2}.

   A -81 C $\dfrac{1}{81}$

   B $-\dfrac{1}{81}$

2. Simplify $x^{-2}y^3$.

   A xy^{-6} C $\dfrac{y^3}{x^2}$

   B xy

3. Simplify $\dfrac{a^{-2}b^4}{c^{-3}}$ completely.

   A $a^2b^4c^3$ C $\dfrac{1}{a^2b^4c^3}$

   B $\dfrac{b^4c^3}{a^2}$

4. Simplify $\dfrac{1}{2^{-3}}$.

   A 8 C $\dfrac{1}{6}$

   B 6

5. Simplify 3^4.

   A 9 C 81

   B 12

6. Simplify 11^{-2}.

   A -121 C $\dfrac{1}{121}$

   B -22

7. Simplify $(-3)^3$

   A -27 C $\dfrac{1}{27}$

   B -9

8. Which expression below is NOT simplified?

   A $\dfrac{a^3}{b^2}$ C $m^{-2}n^4$

   B $-x^3y$

9. Simplify $x^3y^{-4}x^2$.

   A $\dfrac{x^5}{y^4}$ C x^2y^2

   B $\dfrac{x^6}{y^4}$

10. Simplify $9^{\frac{3}{2}}$.

    A 27 C 3

    B 9

11. Simplify $\left(\dfrac{2}{3}\right)^{-3}$.

    A $\dfrac{8}{27}$ C $\dfrac{27}{8}$

    B $\dfrac{4}{9}$

12. Simplify $8^{\frac{4}{3}}$.

    A 4 C 16

    B 12

13. Simplify $64^{\frac{1}{3}}$.

    A 4 C 64

    B 16

14. Simplify $625^{\frac{1}{4}}$.

    A 4 C 6

    B 5

15. Simplify $81^{\frac{3}{4}}$.

    A 3 C 27

    B 9

16. Simplify $(x^{\frac{1}{3}})^6\sqrt[4]{x^4}$. All variables represent nonnegative numbers.

    A x^3 C $x^{2(x)}$

    B x^4

     Holt McDougal Algebra 1

Exponents and Polynomials

CHAPTER 6

Section B Quiz

Select the best answer.

1. What is the degree of $-4xy^2z$?

  A 2   C 4

  B 3

2. What is the degree of $5x^2y^3 + 2x^2$?

  A 2   C 6

  B 5

3. What is the leading coefficient of $2x^2 + 5x^3 + 4x + 3$?

  A 2   C 5

  B 3

4. Which of the following is a cubic binomial?

  A $2x^3 + 4x$

  B $3x^2 + x$

  C $x^3 + 6x^2 + 2$

5. Add $m^2 + 3m^2 + m$.

  A $4m^2 + m$ C $5m^5$

  B $3m^2 + m$

6. Subtract $2xy^3 - 3xy^3$.

  A xy^3 C $-xy^3$

  B $-6xy^3$

7. Add $(4x^3 + 2x) + (8x^3 - 5x + 4)$.

  A $12x^3 - 3x + 4$

  B $12x^3 - 7x + 4$

  C $12x^3 + 3x + 4$

8. Subtract $(9x^4 + x^2) - (6x^4 - 3x^2 - 8)$.

  A $3x^4 - 2x^2 + 8$

  B $3x^4 - 2x^2 - 8$

  C $3x^4 + 4x^2 + 8$

9. Multiply $(8a^3b^2)(2a^2b)$.

  A $16ab$ C $16a^5b^3$

  B $16a^6b^2$

10. Multiply $2xy(x^3 - 3y^2)$.

  A $2x^4y - 6xy^3$

  B $2x^3y - 6xy^2$

  C $2x^4y + 6xy^3$

11. Multiply $(x + 4)(x - 3)$.

  A $x^2 + 7x - 12$

  B $x^2 - x - 12$

  C $x^2 + x - 12$

12. Multiply $(x + 2)(3x^2 - 4x + 5)$.

  A $3x^3 + 2x^2 - 3x + 10$

  B $3x^3 - 4x^2 + 5x + 10$

  C $3x^3 - 2x^2 - 3x + 10$

13. The length of a rectangle is 5 less than the width. Which polynomial describes the area of the rectangle?

  A $w^2 + 5w$ C $5w^2$

  B $w^2 - 5w$

14. Which is NOT a perfect square trinomial?

  A $9a^2 - 42a + 49$

  B $24a^2 + 26a + 9$

  C $144a^2 - 96a + 16$

15. Multiply $(3m + n^2)(3m - n^2)$.

  A $6m^2 - n^4$

  B $6m^2 - 6mn^2 + n^4$

  C $9m^2 - n^4$

Holt McDougal Algebra 1

CHAPTER
6

Exponents and Polynomials
Chapter Test Form A

Select the best answer.

1. Which of the following is equivalent to 6^{-4}?

    A $(-6)^4$

    B $\dfrac{1}{6^4}$

2. Evaluate x^{-3} for $x = 2$.

    A -8

    B -6

    C $\dfrac{1}{8}$

3. Simplify $2\,a^0$.

    A 0

    B 1

    C 2

4. Simplify 1^5.

    A 1

    B 5

5. Simplify 64^0.

    A 0   C 64

    B 1

6. Simplify 16^{-2}.

    A -256

    B $\dfrac{1}{256}$

7. Simplify $16^{\frac{3}{4}}$.

    A 2

    B 4

    C 8

8. Simplify $125^{\frac{1}{3}}$.

    A -5

    B 5

    C 25

9. Simplify $\left(\dfrac{1}{2}\right)^{-4}$.

    A -2

    B $-\dfrac{1}{16}$

    C 16

10. Simplify $\left(\dfrac{1}{64}\right)^{\frac{1}{2}}$.

    A $\dfrac{1}{128}$

    B $\dfrac{1}{8}$

11. Simplify $4^{\frac{5}{2}}$.

    A 10

    B 16

    C 32

12. Simplify $\left(\dfrac{1}{9}\right)^{-\frac{1}{2}}$.

    A 3

    B 81

13. Simplify $\left(\dfrac{5}{9}\right)^{-2}$.

 A $-\dfrac{25}{81}$ B $\dfrac{81}{25}$

14. Simplify the quotient $(8 \times 10^9) \div (2 \times 10^3)$.

 A 4×10^3 B 4×10^6

15. Simplify $16^{\frac{1}{4}}$.

 A 2 B 4

16. Simplify $27^{\frac{2}{3}}$.

 A 9 B 18

17. Simplify $\sqrt[3]{x^6 y^9}$. All variables represent nonnegative numbers.

 A x^5 C $x^{\frac{1}{2}} y^{\frac{1}{3}}$

 B $x^2 y^3$

18. Which polynomial is written in standard form?

 A $-5x^3 + 2x + 9x^2$

 B $-5x^3 + 9x^2 + 2x$

 C $2x + 9x^2 - 5x^3$

19. Classify the polynomial $5x^2 + 9x + 1$ according to its degree.

 A cubic C quadratic

 B linear

20. Evaluate $4w^2 + 3$ for $w = 5$.

 A 103 C 403

 B 112

21. Add $(2x^3 - 5) + (x^3 + 3)$.

 A $3x^3 - 2$

 B $3x^6 - 2$

22. Subtract $(6a^2 + 3a) - (4a^2 + 2a)$.

 A $2a^2 + a$ C 3

 B $2a^2 + 5a$

23. Multiply $(4r^3)(2r^5)$.

 A $8r^8$

 B $8r^{15}$

 C $2048r^8$

24. A rectangle has width w and its length is 2 units longer than the width, or $w + 2$. Write a polynomial for the area of the rectangle.

 A $w^2 + 2$

 B $w^2 + 2w$

 C $2w + 2$

25. Multiply $(x + 2)(x + 3)$.

 A $x^2 + 6$

 B $x^2 + 5x + 6$

26. Multiply $(b + 3)(b^2 + 2b + 1)$.

 A $b^3 + 2b^3 + 3$

 B $b^3 + 5b^2 + 7b + 3$

 C $3b^3 + 6b^2 + 3b$

27. Multiply $(x + 7)(x - 7)$.

 A $x^2 - 49$

 B $x^2 + 14x - 49$

28. Which product results in $x^2 + 10x + 25$?

 A $(x - 5)^2$

 B $(x + 5)^2$

 C $(x + 5)(x - 5)$

LESSON **Practice A**
7-1
Factors and Greatest Common Factors

Complete the prime factorization of each number. The first one is done for you.

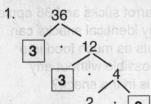

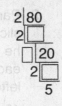

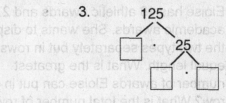

$3^2 \cdot 2^2$

Find the GCF of each pair of numbers. The first one is done for you.

4. 15 and 40

5. 8 and 32

_____ 5 _____

6. 36 and 48

7. 50 and 75

Find the GCF of each pair of monomials. The first one is done for you.

8. $12y^3$ and $15y^2$

9. $3p^4$ and $4p$

$3y^2$

10. $18x^6$ and $24y^2$

11. $14xy^2$ and $21y^3$

Mrs. Graham has 64 math problems written on blue paper and 48 problems written on red paper. She needs to sort the papers and place them in envelopes so that each envelope has the same number of pieces and no envelope has both red and blue pieces.

12. If Mrs. Graham puts the greatest possible number of papers in each envelope, how many papers will go in each envelope? (*Hint:* What is the GCF of 64 and 48?) _____

13. How many envelopes can Mrs. Graham create if she puts the greatest possible number of papers in each envelope? _____

Holt McDougal Algebra 1

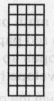

LESSON 7-1

Problem Solving

Factors and Greatest Common Factors

Write the correct answer.

1. Eloise has 18 athletic awards and 27 academic awards. She wants to display the two types separately but in rows of equal length. What is the greatest number of awards Eloise can put in each row? What is the total number of rows?

Solution:

18 athletic	$2 \times 3 \times 3$
27 academic:	$3 \times 3 \times 3$
GCF: 9	9 awards in each row

$18 + 27 = 45$

$45 \div 9 = 5$

5 rows

2. Parker has 48 carrot sticks and 36 apple slices. How many identical snacks can he make if he puts as much food into each snack as possible without any leftovers? What is in the snack?

48: $2 \cdot 2 \cdot 2 \cdot 2 \cdot 3$

36: $2 \cdot 2 \cdot 3 \cdot 3$

_____

_____

Part of an ad for foam squares is shown below. Use it to answer questions 3–5. Select the best answer.

3. Tom uses one package to make a rectangle different from the one shown. Which could be its dimensions?

  A 2×18

  B 3×16

  C 4×8

4. Jody has 2 packages of red, 6 packages of blue, and half a package of yellow squares. She wants to build a rectangle so that each row is the same color. What is the greatest number of squares per row?

  F 2

  G 6

  H 18

Each package comes with 36 foam squares that interlock for a safe, colorful floor mat! You can make a ...

square   rectangle   or any shape you want!

5. In problem 4, how many rows will be blue?

  A 2

  B 4

  C 12

Holt McDougal Algebra 1

Practice A
Factoring by GCF

Factor each polynomial. Check your answer. The first one is done for you.

1. $x^2 + 5x$

  $x(\ \underline{x}\ + \underline{5}\ )$

2. $5m^3 + 45$

  ___ (___ + 9)

3. $15y^3 + 20y^5 - 10$

  ___ $(3y^3 + 4$ ___ - ___ $)$

4. $10y^2 + 12y^3$

_____

5. $-12t^5 + 6t$

_____

6. $6x^4 + 15x^3 + 3x^2$

_____

7. The expression $-5t^2 + 40t$ gives the approximate
   height of a golf ball after t seconds at a speed of
   40 m/s. Factor this expression.

   _____

Factor out the common binomial factor in each expression.

8. $4d(d + 2) + 9(d + 2)$

_____

9. $12(x - 5) + 7x(x - 5)$

_____

Factor each polynomial by grouping.

10. $n^3 + 3n^2 + 4n + 12$

   $(n^3 + \underline{\ \ })+ (4n + \underline{\ \ })$

   $n^2(n + \underline{\ \ }) + 4(n + \underline{\ \ })$

   _____

11. $2x^3 + 5x^2 + 2x + 5$

Factor each polynomial by grouping and using opposites.

12. $2y^3 - 4y^2 + 6 - 3y$

   $(\underline{\ \ } - 4y^2) + (\underline{\ \ } - 3y)$

   $2y^2 (\underline{\ \ } - 2) + 3 (\underline{\ \ } - y)$

   $2y^2 (\underline{\ \ } - 2) + 3(-1) (\underline{\ \ } - 2)$

   $2y^2 (\underline{\ \ } - 2) - 3(y - \underline{\ \ })$

   _____

13. $4m^3 - 12m^2 + 15 - 5m$

LESSON 7-2 **Problem Solving**

Factoring by GCF

Write the correct answer.

1. The area of a rug, which is shaped like a rectangle, is $4x^2 + 4x$ square feet. Factor this polynomial to find the dimensions of the rug.

   Solution:

   $A = 4x^2 + 4x$

   $= 4x(x + 1)$

   Dimensions: $4x$, $x + 1$

2. The number of customers visiting a local museum since the year 2000 can be modeled by the expression $-3x^2 - 27x + 825$, where x is the number of years since 2000. Factor this polynomial.

The diagram shows four sections of an herb garden. Use the figure to answer questions 3–5. Select the best answer.

3. The section where rosemary grows is square and has an area of $4x^2$ square feet. What is the length of one side?

   A x feet

   B x^2 feet

   C $2x$ feet

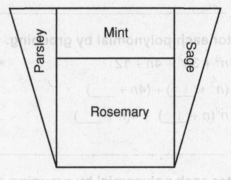

4. Rosemary and mint cover $6x^2 - 2x$ square feet. The width of this section is the side of the square of rosemary. What is the length of the section?

   F $2x$ feet

   G $x - 1$ feet

   H $3x - 1$ feet

5. The parsley and sage sections each have an area of $\frac{1}{2}(3x^2 - 6x - x + 2)$ square feet. Factor $3x^2 - 6x - x + 2$. What are the base and height of each triangular section?

   A $2x - 3$ feet; $x^2 + 1$ feet

   B $3x - 1$ feet; $x - 2$ feet

   C $3x - 1$ feet; $x^2 - 2$ feet

LESSON 7-3

Practice A
Factoring $x^2 + bx + c$

Factor each trinomial. The first one is done for you.

1. $x^2 + 5x + 6$ 2. $x^2 + 5x + 4$ 3. $x^2 + 9x + 20$

     __$(x + 3)(x + 2)$__   _____$(x + \quad)(x + \quad)$_____   _____$(x + \quad)(x + \quad)$_____

4. $x^2 + 10x + 21$ 5. $x^2 + 11x + 30$ 6. $x^2 + 10x + 16$

_____   _____   _____

7. $x^2 - 8x + 12$ 8. $x^2 - 8x + 15$ 9. $x^2 - 17x + 16$

     _____$(x - \quad)(x - \quad)$_____   _____$(x - \quad)(x - \quad)$_____   _____$(x - \quad)(x - \quad)$_____

10. $x^2 - 12x + 27$ 11. $x^2 - 15x + 44$ 12. $x^2 - 13x + 40$

_____   _____   _____

13. $x^2 + 6x - 40$ 14. $x^2 + 2x - 3$ 15. $x^2 + 4x - 32$

     _____$(x + \quad)(x - \quad)$_____   _____$(x + \quad)(x - \quad)$_____   _____$(x + \quad)(x - \quad)$_____

16. $x^2 + 10x - 24$ 17. $x^2 + 12x - 28$ 18. $x^2 + 3x - 10$

     _____$(x + \quad)(x - \quad)$_____   _____$(x + \quad)(x - \quad)$_____   _____$(x + \quad)(x - \quad)$_____

19. $x^2 - 2x - 15$ 20. $x^2 - 8x - 20$ 21. $x^2 - 2x - 48$

_____   _____   _____

LESSON 7-3

Problem Solving

Factoring $x^2 + bx + c$

Write the correct answer.

1. A plot of land is rectangular and has an area of $x^2 - 5x - 24$ m^2. The length is $x + 3$ m. Find the width of the plot.

   Solution:

   $x^2 - 5x - 24 = (x + 3)(x - 8)$

   $3 \cdot -8 = -24, 3x + (-8x) = -5x$

   The width is the shorter of $x - 8$ m.

2. The area of a poster board is $x^2 + 3x - 10$ inches. The width is $x - 2$ inches.

   a. Write an expression for the length of the poster board.

   $x^2 + 3x - 10 = (x - 2)$ _____

   Length: _____

   b. Find the dimensions of the poster board when $x = 14$.

   _____

The figure shows the plans for a patio at the back of a house. Use the figure to answer questions 3–5. Select the best answer.

3. The area of the patio is $(x^2 + 10x - 200)$ ft^2. What is its length?

   A $(x - 20)$ feet

   B $(x + 2)$ feet

   C $(x + 20)$ feet

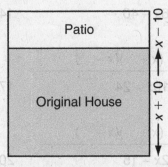

Patio

Original House

$x - 10$

$x + 10$

4. What is the area of the original house?

   F $(x^2 + 8x - 20)$ ft^2

   G $(x^2 + 12x + 200)$ ft^2

   H $(x^2 + 30x + 200)$ ft^2

5. The homeowners decide to make the patio bigger. The area of the patio is now $(x^2 + 12x - 160)$ ft^2. By how many feet was the width of the patio extended?

   A 1 foot

   B 2 feet

   C 3 feet

LESSON 7-4 Practice A

Factoring $ax^2 + bx + c$

Factor each trinomial, where c is positive. The first one is done for you.

1. $5x^2 + 17x + 6$

$(1x + 3)(5x + 2)$

2. $4x^2 + 16x + 15$

$(2x + \quad)(2x + \quad)$

3. $3x^2 + 17x + 20$

_____

4. $6x^2 + 19x + 10$

5. $8x^2 + 18x + 7$

6. $8x^2 + 14x + 3$

7. $4x^2 - 33x + 8$

$(4x - \quad)(\ x - \quad)$

8. $9x^2 - 27x + 14$

$(3x - \quad)(3x - \quad)$

9. $6x^2 - 25x + 25$

10. $5x^2 - 22x + 8$

11. $21x^2 - 22x + 5$

12. $12x^2 - 25x + 12$

Factor each trinomial, where c is negative. The first one is done for you.

13. $10x^2 + 13x - 9$

$(5x + 9)(2x - 1)$

14. $3x^2 + x - 4$

$(3x + \quad)(\ x - \quad)$

15. $5x^2 + 7x - 6$

16. $4x^2 - 9x - 9$

17. $4x^2 - 12x - 7$

18. $6x^2 - 7x - 20$

Factor each trinomial, where a is negative. The first one is done for you.

19. $-5x^2 - 48x - 27$

$-1(5x^2 + 48x + 27)$

$-1(5x + 3)(1x + 9)$

20. $-6x^2 + 11x - 4$

$-1(2x - \quad)(3x - \quad)$

21. $-20x^2 + 7x + 6$

LESSON 7-4

Problem Solving
Factoring ax² + bx + c

$Factoring\ ax^2 + bx + c$

Write the correct answer.

1. A rectangular painting has an area of $(2x^2 + 8x + 6)$ cm². Its length is $(2x + 2)$ cm. Find the width of the painting.

   Solution:

   $A = 2x^2 + 8x + 6$

   $= (2x + 2)(x + 3)$

   The width is $x + 3$ cm.

2. A ball is kicked straight up into the air. The height of the ball in feet is given by the expression $-16t^2 + 12t + 4$, where t is time in seconds. Factor the expression. Then find the height of the ball after 1 second.

   $(16t^2 - 12t - 4) = - (4t - \underline{\quad})(4t + \underline{\quad})$

   _____

Select the best answer.

3. The area of a soccer field is $(24x^2 + 100x + 100)$ m². The width of the field is $(4x + 10)$ m. What is the length?

   A $(3x + 10)$ m

   B $(6x + 1)$ m

   C $(6x + 10)$ m

4. A square parking lot has an area of $(4x^2 + 20x + 25)$ ft². What is the length of one side of the parking lot?

   F $(2x + 5)$ ft

   G $(2x + 10)$ ft

   H $(5x + 4)$ ft

5. For a certain college, the number of applications received after x months is given by the polynomial $3x^2 + 490x + 6000$. What is this expression in factored form?

   A $(3x - 40)(x - 150)$

   B $(3x + 40)(x + 150)$

   C $(3x - 30)(x - 200)$

LESSON 7-5

Practice A
Factoring Special Products

Factor each perfect square trinomial by filling in the blanks. The first one is done for you.

1.

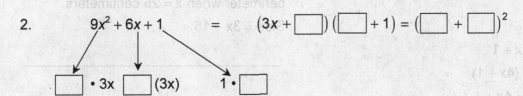

$x^2 + 10x + 25 = (x+5)(x + \boxed{5}) = (\boxed{x} + \boxed{5})^2$

$x \cdot x \quad 2(x \cdot 5) \quad 5 \cdot 5$

2. $9x^2 + 6x + 1 = (3x + \boxed{})(\boxed{} + 1) = (\boxed{} + \boxed{})^2$

$\boxed{} \cdot 3x \quad \boxed{} (3x) \quad 1 \cdot \boxed{}$

Factor each perfect square trinomial.

3. $x^2 - 18x + 81$ _____

4. $36x^2 + 24x + 4$ _____

Complete the following sentences. The first one is done for you.

5. $4x^2 + 12x + 36$ is not a perfect square trinomial because

$$12x \neq 2(2x \cdot 6).$$

6. $x^2 + 6x + 6$ is not a perfect square trinomial because

_____

7. A square floor tile has an area of $(x^2 + 8x + 16)$ in^2. The side length of the tile is of the form $cx + d$, where c and d are whole numbers.

a. Find an expression for the side length of the tile. _____

b. Find an expression for the perimeter of the tile. _____

Factor each binomial into the difference of two squares.

8. $x^2 - 9 = (x + \boxed{})(x - \boxed{})$

9. $4p^2 - 49 = (\boxed{} + \boxed{})(\boxed{} - \boxed{})$

10. $t^6 - 144$ _____

11. $16x^{10} - y^2$ _____

Complete the following sentence.

12. $25n^2 - 20$ is not a difference of perfect squares because

_____

_____

Holt McDougal Algebra 1

LESSON 7-5 — Problem Solving

Factoring Special Products

Write the correct answer.

1. A rectangular fountain has an area of $(16x^2 + 8x + 1)$ ft². The dimensions of the rectangle have the form $ax + b$, where a and b are whole numbers. Write an expression for the perimeter of the fountain. Then find the perimeter when $x = 2$ feet.

   Solution:

   $A = 16x^2 + 8x + 1$

   $= (4x + 1)(4x + 1)$

   Side length $= 4x + 1$

   Perimeter $= 4(4x + 1) = 16x + 4$

   When $x = 2$ ft, $P = 36$ ft

2. A square tabletop has an area of $(9x^2 - 90x + 225)$ cm². The dimensions of the tabletop have the form $cx - d$, where c and d are whole numbers. Write an expression for the perimeter of the tabletop. Then find the perimeter when $x = 25$ centimeters.

   Side $= 3x - 15$

   _____

   _____

Nelson is making open top boxes by cutting out corners from a sheet of cardboard, folding the edges up, and then taping them together. Select the best answer.

3. Nelson cut corners so that each corner was a square with side lengths of 4. What is the total area of the base of the box? (*Hint:* A side is $x - 8$.)

   A $x^2 - 8x + 16$

   B $x^2 + 8x + 16$

   C $x^2 - 16x + 64$

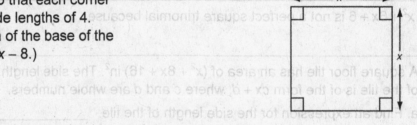

4. What are the dimensions of the square corners if the total remaining area is $x^2 - 4x + 4$?

   F 1 by 1   H 4 by 4

   G 2 by 2

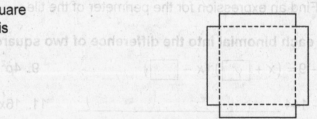

Holt McDougal Algebra 1

LESSON 7-6

Practice A

Choosing a Factoring Method

Tell whether each polynomial is completely factored. If not, factor it. The first one is done for you.

1. $2(n^3 + 4n^2)$

    _____ **no; $2n^2(n + 4)$** _____

2. $3(b^3 - 5)$

    _____

3. $8y(y^2 + 1)$

    _____

4. $(t - 6)(3t + 5)$

    _____

5. $2(m^2 + 10m + 9)$

    _____

6. $(2p - 8)(p + 3)$

    _____

Factor out a GCF. Then continue to factor by using other methods. The first one is done for you.

7. $45g^2 - 20$

    _____ **$5(3g + 2)(3g - 2)$** _____

8. $3w^3 + 30w^2 + 75w$

    _____

9. $12x^2y - 48xy + 48y$

    _____

10. $-3d^3 + 300d$

    _____

11. $2a^2 - 32$

    _____

12. $5m^2 - 5m - 60$

    _____

Factor completely. The first one is done for you.

13. $c^2 + 7c - 18$

    _____ **$(c + 9)(c - 2)$** _____

14. $2x^2 + 8x + 6$

    _____

15. $f^3 - 3f^2 + 4f - 12$

    _____

16. $-6k^2 + 39k - 18$

    _____

Holt McDougal Algebra 1

LESSON
7-6

Problem Solving

Choosing a Factoring Method

Write the correct answer.

1. A rectangular stage set up in a theater has an area of $(15x^2 + 3x - 12)$ square feet. Factor the polynomial completely.

   Solution:

   $A = 15x^2 + 3x - 12$

   $= 3(5x^2 + x - 4)$

   $= 3(5x - 4)(x + 1)$

2. The area of a circular rug is $(16\pi k^2 - 16\pi k + 4\pi)$ m². Factor the expression completely. Then find the area of the rug if $k = 1$ meter.

   _____

   _____

Select the best answer.

3. The volume of a box can be modeled by the expression $7x^4 - 28$. Which shows this expression completely factored?

   A $7(x^2 - 2)^2$

   B $(7x^2 + 4)(x^2 - 7)$

   C $7(x^2 + 2)(x^2 - 2)$

5. The money made from the sales of x mountain bikes is approximated by $20x^2 + 10x + 90$. Factor the expression completely.

   A $2(10x + 9)(x + 5)$

   B $5(4x^2 + 2x + 18)$

   C $10(2x^2 + x + 9)$

4. The area of a rock garden is $(30x^2 + 3x - 6)$ square feet. Factor the polynomial completely.

   F $3(10x^2 + x - 2)$

   G $3(2x + 1)(5x - 2)$

   H $(6x + 3)(5x - 2)$

6. The height of a thrown rock, in meters, can be approximated by $-5t^2 + 5t + 24$, where t is the time in seconds after it was thrown. Completely factor the expression.

   F $-5(t^2 + t + 24)$

   G $-1(5t + 8)(t + 3)$

   H The expression cannot be factored.

CHAPTER 7

Factoring Polynomials

Section A Quiz

Select the best answer.

1. Which of the following is the prime factorization of 60?

   A $2^2 \cdot 3 \cdot 5$ C $3 \cdot 4 \cdot 5$

   B $2^2 \cdot 15$

2. Which of the following could NOT be a prime factorization of any number?

   F 7   H $3 \cdot 6$

   G 2^3

3. What is the GCF of 12 and 32?

   A 2   C 6

   B 4

4. What is the GCF of $10x^2$ and $15x$?

   F 5   H 10

   G $5x$

5. What is the correct factorization of $6x^2 + 24x$?

   A $3(2x^2 + 8x)$ C $6x(x + 4)$

   B $6(x^2 + 4x)$

6. What is the complete factorization of $8y^3 - 4y^2 + 10y$?

   F $y(8y^2 - 4y + 10)$

   G $2(4y^3 - 2y^2 + 5y)$

   H $2y(4y^2 - 2y + 5)$

7. What is the correct factorization of $5(x + 2) - 3x(x + 2)$?

   A $(5x + 10) - (3x^2 + 6x)$

   B $(5 - 3x)(x + 2)$

   C $(5x + 2)(-3x + 2)$

8. Which is another way to write $(5 - x)$?

   F $x - 5$ H $-1(x - 5)$

   G $-1(5 - x)$

9. What is the correct factorization of $x^2 + 13x + 30$?

   A $(x + 1)(x + 30)$ C $(x + 3)(x + 10)$

   B $(x + 2)(x + 15)$

10. What is the correct factorization of $x^2 - 11x + 18$?

    F $(x + 2)(x - 9)$ H $(x - 2)(x - 9)$

    G $(x - 2)(x + 9)$

11. What is the correct factorization of $x^2 - 2x - 15$?

    A $(x + 5)(x - 3)$ C $(x + 5)(x + 3)$

    B $(x - 5)(x + 3)$

12. What value of b would make $x^2 + bx - 24$ factorable?

    F 4   H 8

    G 5

13. What is the correct factorization of $3x^2 + 14x + 8$?

    A $(3x + 4)(x + 2)$ C $(3x + 8)(x + 1)$

    B $(3x + 2)(x + 4)$

14. What is the correct factorization of $2x^2 + 3x - 5$?

    F $(2x + 5)(x - 1)$ H $(2x + 1)(x - 5)$

    G $(2x - 5)(x + 1)$

15. What is the correct factorization of $-5x^2 + 9x + 2$?

    A $-1(5x - 1)(x + 2)$

    B $-1(5x + 1)(x - 2)$

    C $-1(5x - 2)(x + 1)$

16. The area of a rectangle is $12x^2 - 8x - 15$. The width is $(2x - 3)$. What is the length of the rectangle?

    F $(6x - 5)$ H $(2x - 3)$

    G $(6x + 5)$

CHAPTER 7

Factoring Polynomials
Section B Quiz

Select the best answer.

1. Which of the following is a perfect square trinomial?

    A $x^2 + 10x + 25$ C $x^2 + 10x + 20$

    B $x^2 + 5x + 10$

2. Which value of b would make $16x^2 - bx + 25$ a perfect square trinomial?

    F 5   H 40

    G 20

3. What is the complete factorization of $x^2 - 8x + 16$?

    A $(x + 4)(x + 4)$ C $(x + 8)(x + 8)$

    B $(x - 4)(x - 4)$

4. The area of a square garden is $36x^2 - 60x + 25$. What is the perimeter of the garden if $x = 3$ feet?

    F 52 feet   H 92 feet

    G 72 feet

5. What is the correct factorization of $9x^2 - 60xy + 100y^2$?

    A $(3x - 10y)(3x - 10y)$

    B $(3x + 10y)(3x + 10y)$

    C $(6x - 10y)(6x - 10y)$

6. Which of the following binomials is a difference of squares?

    F $x^2 - 6$ H $4x^2 - 1$

    G $5x^2 - 10$

7. What is the complete factorization of $25x^2 - 36$?

    A $(5x + 6)(5x + 6)$

    B $(5x - 6)(5x - 6)$

    C $(5x + 6)(5x - 6)$

8. Which of the following polynomials is completely factored?

    F $(3x + 12)(x - 3)$ H $5x^3 - 4x$

    G $(4x + 9)(x + 5)$

9. Which method could be used to factor $9x^2 + 24x + 16$?

    A Factor out the GCF

    B Factor by grouping

    C Perfect square trinomial

10. Which method could be used to factor $4x^2 - 50$?

    F Factor out the GCF

    G Factor by grouping

    H Perfect square trinomial

11. What is the complete factorization of $x^4 - 1$?

    A $(x^2 + 1)(x^2 - 1)$

    B $(x + 1)^2 (x - 1)^2$

    C $(x^2 + 1)(x - 1)(x + 1)$

12. What is the complete factorization of $4x^2 + 32x + 64$?

    F $4(x + 4)^2$ H $(2x + 8)^2$

    G $2(x + 4)(2x + 8)$

13. Which of the following polynomials is unfactorable?

    A $25x^2 - y^2$ C $x^2 + 3x + 4$

    B $21x + 28$

14. What is the complete factorization of $10x^3 - 35x^2 - 20x$?

    F $(2x + 1)(x - 4)$

    G $5x(2x^2 - 7x - 4)$

    H $5x(2x + 1)(x - 4)$

CHAPTER
7

Factoring Polynomials
Chapter Test Form A

Select the best answer.

1. Which is the prime factorization of 24?

   A $2 \cdot 2 \cdot 2 \cdot 3$

   B $4 \cdot 6$

2. Find the GCF of 12 and 30.

   A 2   C 6

   B 3

3. Find the GCF of $5x^3$ and $15x$.

   A $5x$ C $15x$

   B $5x^3$

4. Shadé is organizing the members of a chorus into rows. The chorus consists of 70 women and 42 men. Each row will have the same number of people, but women and men will not appear in the same row. If she puts the greatest possible number of people in each row, how many rows will there be?

   A 8

   B 14

5. Factor $16y^2 + 12y$ completely.

   A $2y(8y + 6)$

   B $4(4y^2 + 3y)$

   C $4y(4y + 3)$

6. Factor $n(n + 2) + 7(n + 2)$.

   A $(n + 2)(n + 7)$

   B $2(n + 2)(n + 7)$

7. Factor $a^2 + 3a + 8a + 24$ by grouping.

   A $(a + 3)(a + 8)$

   B $(a^2 + 3a)(8a + 24)$

   C $8a(a + 3)$

8. Factor $x^2 + 12x + 35$.

   A $(x + 1)(x + 35)$

   B $(x + 5)(x + 7)$

9. Factor $x^2 - 23x + 22$.

   A $(x - 2)(x - 11)$

   B $(x - 1)(x - 22)$

   C $(x + 1)(x - 23)$

10. Factor $x^2 + 13x - 13$.

    A $(x - 1)(x + 13)$

    B $(x + 1)(x + 12)$

    C cannot be factored

11. Which value of b would make $x^2 + bx - 16$ factorable?

    A -10

    B -6

12. Write the factored form of the polynomial that is modeled by this geometric diagram.

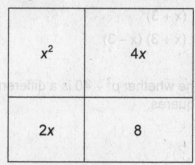

x^2	$4x$
$2x$	8

    A $(x + 1)(x + 8)$

    B $(x + 2)(x + 4)$

    C $(x^2 + 4x)(2x + 8)$

Holt McDougal Algebra 1

Factoring Polynomials

Chapter Test Form A *continued*

13. Factor $2x^2 + 23x + 11$.

    A $(x + 1)(2x + 11)$

    B $(2x + 1)(x + 11)$

14. Factor $5a^2 - 3a - 2$.

    A $(a - 2)(5a + 1)$

    B $(a - 1)(5a + 2)$

    C $(a + 1)(5a - 2)$

15. Which value of c would NOT make $2x^2 + 5x + c$ factorable?

    A -2

    B -3

16. Determine whether $n^2 + 20n + 100$ is a perfect square trinomial.

    A yes

    B no

17. Determine whether $x^2 - 6x - 9$ is a perfect square trinomial.
If so, choose the correct factorization.

    A yes; $(x + 3)^2$

    B yes; $(x + 3)(x - 3)$

    C no

18. Determine whether $p^2 - 40$ is a difference of two squares.

    A yes

    B no

19. Determine whether $x^2 - 16$ is a difference of two squares.
If so, choose the correct factorization.

    A yes; $(x - 4)^2$

    B yes; $(x + 4)(x - 4)$

    C yes; $(x + 4)^2$

20. The area of a square is represented by $z^2 + 10z + 25$.
Which expression represents the perimeter of the square?

    A $z + 9$

    B $2z + 10$

    C $4z + 20$

21. Is $5x(x^2 + 36)$ completely factored?

    A yes; the polynomial is completely factored.

    B no; $x^2 + 36$ can be factored into two binomials.

22. Completely factor $x^4 + 2x^3 - 15x^2$.

    A $(x^2 + 5x)(x^2 - 3x)$

    B $x^2(x + 5)(x - 3)$

23. Completely factor $4m^4 - 324$.

    A $(4m^2 + 36)(m^2 - 9)$

    B $4(m^2 + 9)(m + 3)(m - 3)$

    C $4(m + 3)^2(m + 3)(m - 3)$

Holt McDougal Algebra 1

LESSON 8-1

Practice A

Identifying Quadratic Functions

Tell whether each function is quadratic. Explain.

1.

x	1	2	3	4	5
y	0	3	8	15	24

2. $y + 5 = 2x^2$

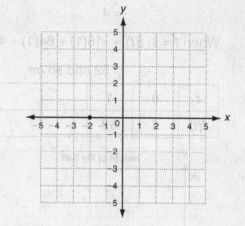

quadratic:
function of the form
$y = ax^2 + bx + c$

<u>_____ **yes** _____</u>

<u>**The second differences are constant.**</u>

3. Use the table of values to graph $y = x^2 - 4$.

x	$y = x^2 - 4$	(x, y)
-2	$y = (-2)^2 - 4 = 0$	(-2, 0)
-1		
0		
1		
2		

Tell whether the graph of each quadratic function opens upward or downward.

4. $y = -5x^2$

5. $y = 2x^2 + 7$

Use the graph of the quadratic function below for questions 6–8.

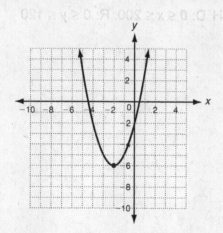

6. Identify the vertex of the parabola.

7. Give the minimum or maximum value.

8. Find the domain and range.

Holt McDougal Algebra 1

LESSON	**Problem Solving**
8-1	*Identifying Quadratic Functions*

Write the correct answer.

1. The function $f(t) = -16t^2 + 64t + 4$ describes the height of a softball in feet. Make a table of values for the function and then graph it.

   Solution:

   When $t = 0$, $f(t) = -16(0)^2 + 64(0) + 4$

   $= 4$

   When $t = 1$, $f(t) = -16(1) + 64(1) + 4$

   $= 52$ and so on.

t	0	1			
$f(t)$	4	52			

   Height of Fly Ball

   (graph with y-axis "Height (ft)" from 0 to 80, x-axis "Time (s)" from 0 to 6)

2. Jorge recorded the number of customers y that came to his store over a number of hours x. Does the data represent a quadratic function? Explain.

x	1	3	5	7	9
y	2	5	11	17	23

   _____

   _____

Radio telescopes are built in the shape of a parabola. The graph below shows a radio telescope dish in cross-section. Select the best answer.

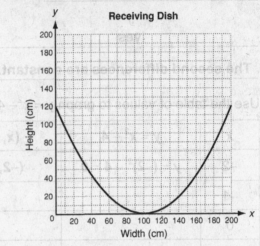

Receiving Dish

(graph with y-axis "Height (cm)" from 0 to 200, x-axis "Width (cm)" from 0 to 200)

3. What is the vertex of this parabola?

   A (0, 120)

   B (100, 0)

   C (200, 120)

4. What are the domain and range of this function?

   F D: all real numbers
   R: all real numbers

   G D: $x \geq 0$, R: $y \geq 0$

   H D: $0 \leq x \leq 200$, R: $0 \leq y \leq 120$

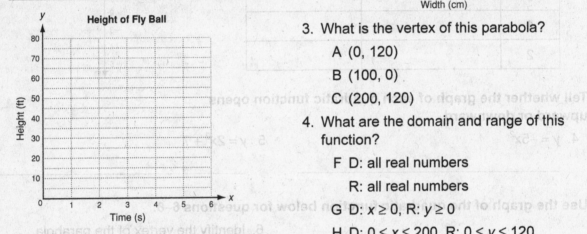

Holt McDougal Algebra 1

LESSON
8-2

Practice A
Characteristics of Quadratic Functions

**Find the zeros of each quadratic function from its graph.
The first one is done for you.**

1.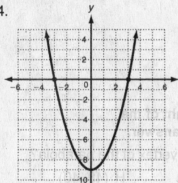

    _____
    −4 and 0

2.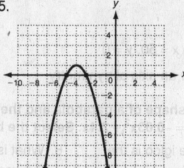

    _____

3.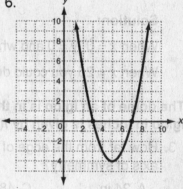

    _____

Find the axis of symmetry of each parabola. The first one is done for you.

4.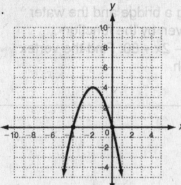

    _____
    x = 0

5.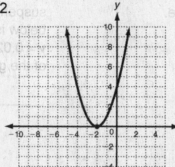

    _____

6.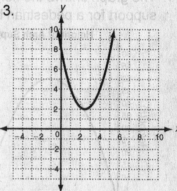

    _____

**Find the axis of symmetry and the vertex of each quadratic function
by completing the following. The first one is done for you.**

7. $y = x^2 + 8x + 12$

    Find a: _____**1**_____

    Find b: _____**8**_____

    Find $-\dfrac{b}{2a}$. ____**−4**____

    Axis of symmetry: **x = −4**

    Vertex: ____**(−4, −4)**____

8. $y = x^2 - 10x + 40$

    Find a: _____

    Find b: _____

    Find $-\dfrac{b}{2a}$. _____

    Axis of symmetry: _____

    Vertex: _____

9. $y = 2x^2 - 8x - 3$

    Find a:_____

    Find b: _____

    Find $-\dfrac{b}{2a}$. _____

    Axis of symmetry: _____

    Vertex: _____

Holt McDougal Algebra 1

LESSON
8-2
Problem Solving
Characteristics of Quadratic Functions

Write the correct answer.

1. The graph shows the height of an arch support for a pedestrian bridge.

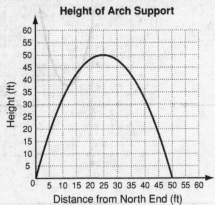

Height of Arch Support

Distance from North End (ft)

Find the zeros (if any) and axis of symmetry of this parabola.

Solution:

When $x = 0$, $y = 0$ and when $x = 50$, $y = 0$

When $x = 25$ you could draw an axis of symmetry.

2. The distance between the cables suspending a bridge and the water below is given by the function $y = 0.02x^2 - 2x + 80$. Find the vertex of the graph.

_____

The dome of an igloo is in the shape of a parabola and the height of the igloo in inches is given by $f(x) = -0.03x^2 + 2.4x$. Select the best answer.

3. How far from the edge of the igloo is the axis of symmetry?

   A 24 in.   C 48 in.

   B 40 in.

4. How tall is the center of the igloo? (*Hint:* the top of the igloo is the vertex of the parabola.)

   F 24 in.   H 48 in.

   G 40 in.

5. Looks at the zeros to see how wide the igloo is. What are the zeros of this parabola?

   A −80 and 80   C 0 and 80

   B −40 and 40

6. What is the vertex of the parabola?

   F (20, 36)   H (48, 40)

   G (40, 48)   J (80, 0)

7. Which graph below is the graph of the function?

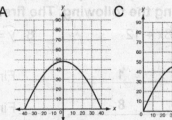

A   C

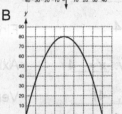

B

LESSON 8-3 Practice A
Graphing Quadratic Functions

Identify the following components of each quadratic function. Then graph the function. The first one is started for you.

1. $y = x^2 + 2x - 3$

   axis of symmetry $x = -\dfrac{b}{2a}$: _____ $x = -1$ _____

   vertex $\left(-\dfrac{b}{2a}, y \right)$: _____ **(−1, −4)** _____

   y-intercept (c): _____

   two other points: _____

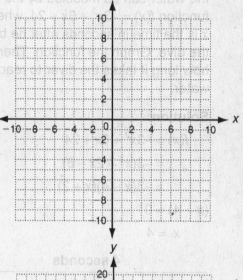

2. $y = -2x^2 - 8x + 10$

   axis of symmetry $x = -\dfrac{b}{2a}$: _____

   vertex $\left(-\dfrac{b}{2a}, y \right)$: _____

   y-intercept (c): _____

   two other points: _____

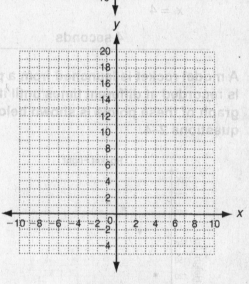

3. The height in feet of a dolphin as it jumps out of the water can be modeled by the function $f(x) = -16x^2 + 32x$, where x is the time in seconds after it exits the water.

   Find the dolphin's maximum height and the time it takes to reach this height. Then find how many seconds the dolphin is in the air.

   maximum height: _____

   time to reach maximum height: _____

   time in the air: _____

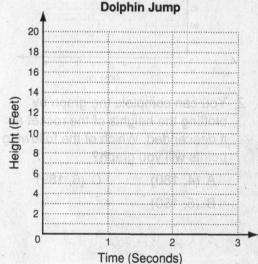

Dolphin Jump

Holt McDougal Algebra 1

Name _____ Date _____ Class_____

Problem Solving
Graphing Quadratic Functions

Write the correct answer.

1. An Olympic diver's height in feet above the water can be modeled by the function $f(x) = -3x^2 + 6x + 24$, where x is the time in seconds after he begins the dive. Graph the function. Then find how long it takes the diver to reach the water.

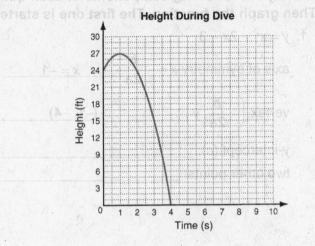

Height During Dive

   Solution:

   $$f(x) = -3x^2 + 6x + 24$$
   $$= -3(x^2 - 2x - 8)$$
   $$= -3(x - 4)(x + 2)$$
   $$(x - 4) = 0$$
   $$x = 4$$

   4 seconds

A model rocket is launched from a platform into the air. Its height is recorded at different times until it reaches its peak at 259 ft. The graph of these points is shown below. Use this graph to answer questions 2–4.

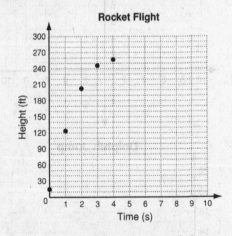

Rocket Flight

2. You can complete the graph by plotting the heights of the rocket as it descended. Which of the following points will you graph?

   A (4, 180)   C (6, 189)

   B (5, 150)

3. Which of the following equations models the flight of the rocket where x is the time in seconds and y is the height in feet?

   F $16x^2 + 15x + 125$

   G $16x^2 + 125x + 15$

   H $-16x^2 + 125x + 15$

4. About long will the rocket be in the air?

   A 4 seconds

   B 6 seconds

   C 8 seconds

LESSON 8-4

Practice A

Transforming Quadratic Functions

Order the functions from narrowest graph to widest. The first one is done for you.

1. $f(x) = 5x^2$; $g(x) = 2x^2$

   _____ **$f(x), g(x)$** _____

2. $f(x) = \frac{1}{2}x^2$; $g(x) = -3x^2$; $h(x) = x^2$

   _____

Compare the graph of each function with the graph of $f(x) = x^2$.
The first one is done for you.

3. $g(x) = x^2 - 3$

   width: _____ **same** _____

   opens up or down: ____ **both open** ____

   _____ **upward** _____

   vertex: ____ **$f(x)$: (0, 0)** ____

   ____ **$g(x)$ down 3 units at (0, –3)** ____

4. $g(x) = \frac{1}{5}x^2$

   width: _____

   opens up or down: _____

   _____

   vertex: _____

5. $g(x) = 2x^2 + 4$

   width: _____

   opens up or down: _____

   _____

   vertex: _____

6. $g(x) = -x^2 - 1$

   width: _____

   opens up or down: _____

   _____

   vertex: _____

7. Two blocks are dropped, one from a height of 400 feet and the other from a height of 256 feet.

   a. Complete the two height functions.

   $h_1(t) = -16t^2 +$ _____

   $h_2(t) = -16t^2 +$ _____

   b. Sketch and compare their graphs.

   The graph of h_2 is a _____ translation

   of the graph of h_1: _____ units down.

   c. Tell when each block reaches the ground.

   _____

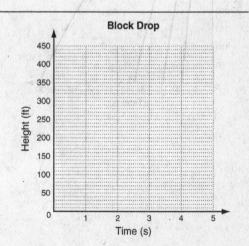

Block Drop

Height (ft) / Time (s)

Holt McDougal Algebra 1

Name _____ Date _____ Class_____

Problem Solving
Transforming Quadratic Functions

Write the correct answer.

1. Two workers working at different heights dropped their hammers at the same time. The first worker was working at a height of 400 ft, the second at a height of 160 ft. Write the two functions that describe the heights of the hammers.

   Solution:

   $y = -16x^2 + 400$

   $y = -16x^2 + 160$

3. Based on the graphs you drew in problem 2, how long will it take each hammer to reach the ground?

   _____

   _____

2. Graph the two functions you found in problem 1 on the grid below.

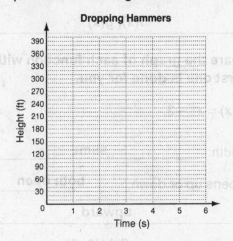

The pull of gravity varies from planet to planet. The graph shows the height of objects dropped from 500 ft on the surface of four planets. Use this graph to answer questions 4–5. Select the best answer.

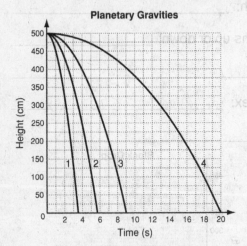

4. Of the four planets, Jupiter has the strongest gravity. Which of the four graphs represents the height of the object dropped on Jupiter?

   F Graph 1   H Graph 4

   G Graph 2

5. Due to its small size, Pluto has a very weak pull of gravity. Which of the equations below represents the graph of the object dropped on Pluto?

   A $h(t) = -16x^2 + 500$

   B $h(t) = -6x^2 + 500$

   C $h(t) = -1.25x^2 + 500$

Name _____ Date _____ Class _____

Practice A
Solving Quadratic Equations by Graphing

Solve each quadratic equation by graphing the related function and finding the zeros. The first one is done for you.

1. $x^2 - 4x + 4 = 0$

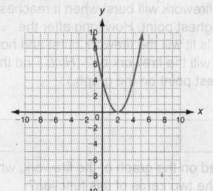

_____ **x = 2** _____

2. $x^2 + x = 6$

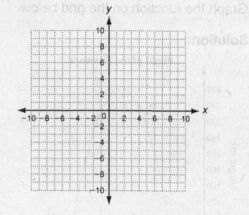

3. $x^2 = 1$

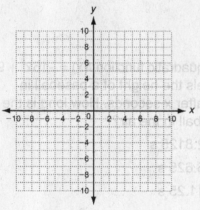

4. $7 + x^2 = 3x$

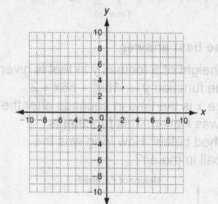

5. You throw a ball straight up in the air. The quadratic function $y = -16x^2 + 48x$ models the height in feet of the ball after x seconds. Use a graphing calculator to sketch the graph of this function. Use the zeros to find how long the ball is in the air.

_____

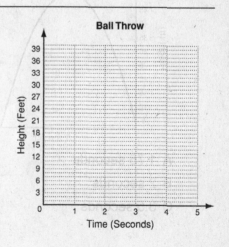

Ball Throw

Holt McDougal Algebra 1

LESSON 8-5 Problem Solving

Solving Quadratic Equations by Graphing

The path of a firework in the air is modeled by the parabolic function $y = -16x^2 + 256x - 624$ where x is the number of seconds after the fuse is lit.

1. Graph the function on the grid below.

Solution:

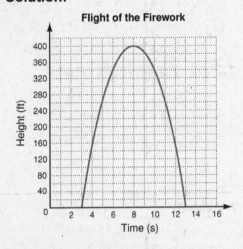

Flight of the Firework

2. The firework will burst when it reaches its highest point. How long after the fuse is lit will the firework burst and how high will the firework be? (*Hint:* Find the highest point on the graph.)

_____

_____

3. Based on the graph of the firework, what are the two zeros of this function?

_____

_____

Select the best answer.

4. The height of a football y in feet is given by the function $y = -16x^2 + 56x + 2$ where x is the time in seconds after the ball was kicked. This function is graphed below. How long was the football in the air?

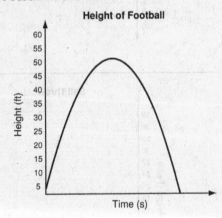

Height of Football

A 1.75 seconds

B 2 seconds

C 3.5 seconds

5. The quadratic function $f(x) = -16x^2 + 90x$ models the height of a baseball in feet after x seconds. How long is the baseball in the air?

F 2.8125 s

G 5.625 s

H 11.25 s

6. The function $y = -0.04x^2 + 2x$ models the height of an arch support for a bridge, where x is the distance in feet from where the arch supports enter the water. How many real solutions does this function have?

A 0

B 1

C 2

Holt McDougal Algebra 1

LESSON 8-6

Practice A

Solving Quadratic Equations by Factoring

1. Complete: If $ab = 0$, then _____ or _____.

Use the Zero Product Property to solve each equation.
Check your answers. The first one is done for you.

2. $(x - 7)(x + 2) = 0$

    $x - 7 = 0$ or $x + 2 = 0$

    $x = \underline{\ 7\ }$ or $x = \underline{\ -2\ }$

3. $(x - 5)(x - 1) = 0$

    $x - 5 = 0$ or $x - 1 = 0$

    $x = \underline{\ \ \ \ }$ or $x = \underline{\ \ \ \ }$

4. $(x + 2)(x + 6) = 0$

5. $(3x - 4)(x - 3) = 0$

_____

_____

Factor each quadratic expression. Then, use the Zero Product
Property to solve the equation. The first one is done for you.

6. $x^2 - 5x = 0$

    $x(\underline{\ x - 5\ }) = 0$

    $x = 0$ or $(\underline{\ x - 5\ }) = 0$

    $x = 0$ or $x = \underline{\ 5\ }$

7. $x^2 + 3x + 2 = 0$

    $(x + 2)(\underline{\ \ \ \ \ \ \ \ }) = 0$

    $x + 2 = 0$ or $(\underline{\ \ \ \ \ \ \ \ }) = 0$

    $x = -2$ or $x = \underline{\ \ \ \ }$

8. $x^2 - 6x - 27 = 0$

    $(x - \underline{\ \ \ \ })(x + \underline{\ \ \ \ }) = 0$

    $(\underline{\ \ \ \ \ \ }) = 0$ or $(\underline{\ \ \ \ \ \ }) = 0$

    $x = \underline{\ \ \ \ }$ or $x = \underline{\ \ \ \ }$

9. $x^2 + 8x + 15 = 0$

    $(\underline{\ \ \ \ \ \ })(\underline{\ \ \ \ \ \ }) = 0$

    $(\underline{\ \ \ \ \ \ }) = 0$ or $(\underline{\ \ \ \ \ \ }) = 0$

    $x = \underline{\ \ \ \ }$ or $x = \underline{\ \ \ \ }$

10. $x^2 - 6x + 5 = 0$

11. $x^2 - 4x - 12 = 0$

_____

_____

12. A package is dropped from a helicopter at 1600 feet. The height
of the package can be modeled by $h = -16t^2 + 1600$, where h is
the height of the package in feet and t is the time in seconds.
How long it will take for the package to hit the ground?

    a. Write the equation. _____

    b. Solve the equation. _____

    c. Answer the equation. _____

                                           Holt McDougal Algebra 1

LESSON 8-6

Problem Solving

Solving Quadratic Equations by Factoring

Write the correct answer.

1. The height of an acorn falling from a tree is $h = -16t^2 + 25$ where h is height in feet and t is time in seconds. How long does it takes for the acorn to reach the ground?

   Solution:

   $$-16t^2 + 25 = 0$$
   $$-16t^2 = -25$$
   $$16t^2 = 25$$
   $$4t = 5$$
   $$t = 1.25$$

   1.25 seconds

2. An architect is designing a building with a right triangular footprint, or base.

   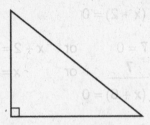

   The hypotenuse of the triangle is 80 feet longer than one leg of the triangle and 40 feet longer than the other leg. Use the Pythagorean Theorem to find the dimensions of the footprint of the building.

   $$(x - 80)^2 + (x - 40)^2 = x^2$$

A store has the shape of a rectangle with a parking lot in the shape of an isosceles trapezoid. The parking lot and the store share a side as shown. Select the best answer.

3. The parking lot has an area of 160 square meters. The shorter base is 4 m longer than the height of the trapezoid, and the longer base is 8 m longer than the height. What is the length of the shorter base?

   A 10 meters

   B 14 meters

   C 18 meters

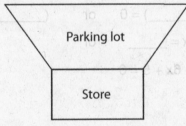

Parking lot

Store

4. The area of the store is 154 square meters. If the depth is given as $\frac{1}{14}x^2 + \frac{15}{14}x$, what is the value of x?

   F 7

   G 11

   H 14

5. What is the depth of the store in meters?

   A 7

   B 11

   C 14

LESSON 8-7 Practice A

Solving Quadratic Equations by Using Square Roots

1. Complete: If $x^2 = a$ and a is a positive real number, then $x =$ _____ or $x =$ _____.

Solve using square roots. Check your answers.
The first one is done for you.

2. $x^2 = 4$

   $x = \pm\sqrt{4}$

   $x = \pm\ \underline{2}$

   The solutions are $\underline{2}$ and $\underline{-2}$.

3. $x^2 = 169$

   $x = \pm\sqrt{\underline{}}$

   $x = \pm\ \underline{}$

   The solutions are _____ and _____.

4. $x^2 = 900$

   $x = \pm\sqrt{\underline{}}$

   $x = \pm\ \underline{}$

5. $x^2 = -121$

   _____

6. $144 = x^2$

   $\pm\sqrt{\underline{}} = x$

   $\pm\ \underline{} = x$

7. $4x^2 = 400$

   $\dfrac{4x^2}{4} = \dfrac{400}{4}$

   $x^2 =$ _____

   $x = \pm\sqrt{\underline{}}$

   $x = \pm\ \underline{}$

8. $x^2 = \dfrac{25}{36}$

   $x^2 = \pm\sqrt{\underline{}}$

   $x = \pm\ \underline{}$

9. $5x^2 + 3 = 128$

   $5x^2 =$ _____

   $x^2 =$ _____

   $x = \pm\sqrt{\underline{}}$

   $x = \pm\ \underline{}$

10. $x^2 - 10 = 26$

11. $8x^2 = 32$

12. $25x^2 - 1 = 0$

_____

Solve. Round to the nearest hundredth. The first one is done for you.

13. $5x^2 = 40$

    ± 2.83

14. $30 - x^2 = 0$

15. $12x^2 - 60 = 0$

16. The area of a square is 225 in².

    a. Write a quadratic equation that can be used to find the dimensions of the square.

    b. Solve the equation. What are the dimensions?

Holt McDougal Algebra 1

LESSON 8-7

Problem Solving

Solving Quadratic Equations by Using Square Roots

A bookcase has the proportions shown in the diagram below. Write the correct answer.

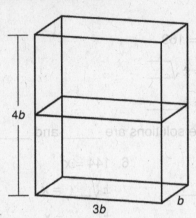

4b

3b

b

1. If the bookcase has two shelves having a total area of 864 square inches, what should *b* equal?

Solution:

$864 \div 2 = 432$, area of one shelf

$3b \cdot b = 432$

$3b^2 = 432$

$b^2 = 144$

$b = 12$

2. What should *b* equal in order for the back of the bookcase to cover an area of 4800 square inches?

_____

3. A collection takes up an area of 400 square inches. What should *b* equal for the top of the bookcase to have the correct area? Round your answer to the nearest tenth of an inch.

_____

Select the best answer.

4. As wall is twice as long as it is high and has an area of 162 square feet. What is the height of the wall?

   A 8 feet

   B 9 feet

   C 12 feet

5. An apple drops off the tree from a height of 8 feet. How long does it take to reach the ground? Use the function $f(x) = -16x^2 + c$, where *c* is the initial height of a falling object.

   F 0.5 seconds

   G 0.71 seconds

   H 1 second

6. A square tablecloth is cut into 4 equal pieces. The area of the tablecloth was 3600 square inches. What is the side length of each equal piece?

   A 20 inches

   B 30 inches

   C 60 inches

Holt McDougal Algebra 1

LESSON
8-8

Practice A

Completing the Square

Complete the square to form a perfect square trinomial.
The first one is done for you.

1. $x^2 + 6x +$ | 9 |

2. $x^2 - 12x +$ | |

3. $x^2 + 8x +$ | |

Solve each equation by completing the square.
The first one is done for you.

4. $x^2 + 6x = -8$

Find $\left(\dfrac{b}{2}\right)^2$: _____ 9 _____

Solutions: _____ −2, −4 _____

5. $x^2 - 6x = -5$

Find $\left(\dfrac{b}{2}\right)^2$: _____

Solutions: _____

6. $x^2 - 2x - 24 = 0$

Find $\left(\dfrac{b}{2}\right)^2$: _____

Solutions: _____

7. $x^2 + 10x + 16 = 0$

Find $\left(\dfrac{b}{2}\right)^2$: _____

Solutions: _____

8. $2x^2 - 8x = 10$

Divide by a: _____

Find $\left(\dfrac{b}{2}\right)^2$: _____

Solutions: _____

9. $3x^2 - 12x - 36 = 0$

Divide by a: _____

Find $\left(\dfrac{b}{2}\right)^2$: _____

Solutions: _____

10. A rectangular patio has an area of 91 ft². The length is 6 feet
longer than the width. Find the dimensions of the patio.
Solve by completing the square.

a. Find the width and the length in terms of w. _____

b. Write an equation for the total area. _____

c. Find $\left(\dfrac{b}{2}\right)^2$. _____

d. Find the dimensions. _____

Holt McDougal Algebra 1

LESSON 8-8 Problem Solving
Completing the Square

Write the correct answer.

1. A room has an area of 176 square feet and is 5 feet longer than it is wide. Find the dimensions of the room.

   Solution:

   $$A = lw$$
   $$176 = (x + 5)x$$
   $$176 = x^2 + 5x$$
   $$x^2 + 5x - 176 = (x + 16)(x - 11)$$
   $$x = 11$$
   $$x + 5 = 16$$

   11 ft by 16 ft

2. A rug is 9 feet long and 7 feet wide. The rug will cover the whole floor except a border that is x feet wide. The area of her room is 167 square feet.

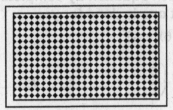

   Find the width of the border, x. Round your answer to the nearest tenth of a foot.

   _____

   _____

Select the best answer.

3. A trapezoid has an area of 1500 square feet. The shorter base of the trapezoid is 15 feet longer than the height. The longer base is 5 feet longer than 3 times the height. What is the length of the longer base?

   A 25 feet

   B 40 feet

   C 80 feet

5. Georgia earned $160 last week. Georgia worked 12 more hours than the amount she is paid per hour. What is Georgia's hourly pay rate?

   A $6.00

   B $8.00

   C $12.00

4. The height of a pumpkin shot from a cannon is given by the function $h = -16t^2 + 240t + 16$ where t is the time in seconds. How many seconds is the pumpkin in the air? Round your answer to the nearest tenth of a second.

   F 7.5 seconds

   G 15.1 seconds

   H 16 seconds

Holt McDougal Algebra 1

LESSON 8-9

Practice A

The Quadratic Formula and the Discriminant

Solve using the quadratic formula. The first one is done for you.

1. $x^2 + 6x + 5 = 0$

   $a:$ $\boxed{1}$ $b:$ $\boxed{6}$ $c:$ $\boxed{5}$

   $x = \dfrac{-\boxed{6} \pm \sqrt{\boxed{6}^2 - 4\boxed{1}\boxed{5}}}{2\boxed{1}}$

   _____
   $-1, -5$

2. $x^2 - 9x + 20 = 0$

   $a:$ $\boxed{}$ $b:$ $\boxed{}$ $c:$ $\boxed{}$

   $x = \dfrac{-\boxed{} \pm \sqrt{\boxed{}^2 - 4\boxed{}\boxed{}}}{2\boxed{}}$

3. $2x^2 + 9x + 4 = 0$

   $a:$ $\boxed{}$ $b:$ $\boxed{}$ $c:$ $\boxed{}$

   _____

4. $x^2 - 3x - 18 = 0$

   $a:$ $\boxed{}$ $b:$ $\boxed{}$ $c:$ $\boxed{}$

   _____

Find the number of real solutions of each equation using the discriminant.
The first one is done for you.

5. $x^2 + 3x + 5 = 0$

   $b^2 - 4ac = \boxed{3}^2 - 4\boxed{1} \cdot \boxed{5}$

   $= \underline{\quad -11 \quad}$

   _____
   no real solutions

6. $x^2 + 10x + 25 = 0$

   $b^2 - 4ac = \boxed{}^2 - 4\boxed{} \cdot \boxed{}$

   $=$ _____

7. $x^2 - 6x - 7 = 0$

   $b^2 - 4ac =$ _____

Solve using any method.

8. $x^2 - 64 = 0$

9. $x^2 + 12x + 36 = 0$

10. $x^2 + 4x - 32 = 0$

11. $2x^2 + 9x - 5 = 0$

Holt McDougal Algebra 1

LESSON
8-9

Problem Solving

The Quadratic Formula and the Discriminant

Write the correct answer.

1. A park has an area for small dogs to play. The length is 15 feet longer than the width and the enclosed area is 1350 square feet. What are the dimensions of the dog's play area?

Solution:

$A = lw$

$1350 = (x + 15)x$

$x^2 + 15x - 1350 = 0$

$x = \dfrac{-15 \pm \sqrt{(15)^2 - 4(-1350)}}{2}$

$= \dfrac{-15 \pm \sqrt{225 - 4(1350)}}{2}$

$= \dfrac{-15 \pm \sqrt{5625}}{2}$

$= \dfrac{-15 \pm 75}{2} = \dfrac{60}{2}$ or $\dfrac{-90}{2}$

Since width is positive $w = \dfrac{60}{2} = 30$.

30 ft by 45 ft

2. A picture frame holds a 4-in. by 6-in. photograph. The frame adds a border x inches wide around three sides of the photo. On the fourth side the frame forms a border that is $3x - 0.5$ in. wide.

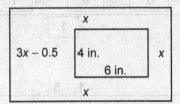

The combined area of the photograph and the frame is 80.5 in^2. Write a quadratic equation for the combined area. Then use the quadratic formula to find x.

_____

_____

The equation $-5x^2 + 72x + 378$ models the number of students enrolled in a school where x is the number of years since the school first opened in 1990. Select the best answer.

3. How many students did the school have when it opened?

   A 68   C 378

   B 72

4. Which equation can be used to find the year in which 502 students were enrolled?

   F $-5x^2 + 72x + 502 = 0$

   G $-5x^2 + 72x - 124 = 0$

   H $-5x^2 + 72x - 502 = 0$

5. In which year were 502 students enrolled?

   A 1992   C 1998

   B 1996

6. Which statement is true?

   F Enrollment exceeded 650 students at one point.

   G Enrollment never exceeded 650 students.

   H The highest enrollment of any year was exactly 650 students.

LESSON 8-10

Practice A

Nonlinear Systems

Solve by graphing. Use a graphing calculator to check your answers.

1. $\begin{cases} y = x^2 - 2 \\ y = 5x - 8 \end{cases}$

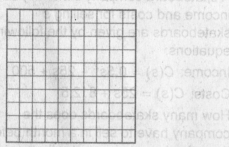

_____

2. $\begin{cases} y = x^2 - 4x + 6 \\ y = -x + 4 \end{cases}$

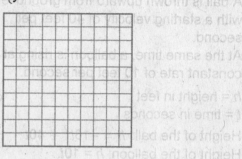

_____

Solve by substitution. Use a graphing calculator to check your answers. The first one is done for you.

3. $\begin{cases} y = x^2 - 3 \\ y = -x + 3 \end{cases}$

(−3, 6), (2, 1)

_____

4. $\begin{cases} y = x^2 - 2x - 3 \\ y = -2x - 5 \end{cases}$

_____

5. $\begin{cases} y = 2x^2 + x - 3 \\ -3x + y = 1 \end{cases}$

_____

6. $\begin{cases} y = x^2 - 25 \\ y = x + 5 \end{cases}$

_____

Solve by elimination. Use a graphing calculator to check your answers. The first one is done for you.

7. $\begin{cases} y = x^2 - 1 \\ 2x - y = -2 \end{cases}$

(−1, 0), (3, 8)

_____

8. $\begin{cases} y = x^2 + 4x + 3 \\ x - y = -1 \end{cases}$

_____

9. $\begin{cases} y = 2x^2 + 4x - 1 \\ 6x + y = -13 \end{cases}$

_____

10. $\begin{cases} y = -x^2 + 3x - 3 \\ 2x - y = 5 \end{cases}$

_____

Holt McDougal Algebra 1

LESSON
8-10

Problem Solving
Nonlinear Systems

Write the correct answer.

1. A ball is thrown upward from ground level with a starting velocity of 40 feet per second.
   At the same time, a balloon is rising at a constant rate of 10 feet per second.

   h = height in feet
   t = time in seconds
   Height of the ball: $h = -16t^2 + 40t$
   Height of the balloon: $h = 10t$.
   Find the time it takes for the ball and the balloon to reach the same height.

   Solution: Set the heights equal, and solve.
   $$-16t^2 + 40t = 10t$$
   $$-16t^2 + 30t = 0$$
   $$-2t(8t + 15) = 0$$
   $$t = 0 \text{ or } t = 1.875$$

   The ball and the balloon are at the same starting height, and at the same height again after 1.875 seconds.

2. A skateboard company's monthly sales income and costs for selling s skateboards are given by the following equations:

   Income: $C(s) = 0.5s^2 + 25s + 500$

   Costs: $C(s) = 25s + 812.5$

   How many skateboards does the company have to sell in a month before the sales income is greater than or equal to the cost?

   Set the equations equal.

   $$0.5s^2 + 25s + 500 = 25s + 812.5$$

   Set one side equal to 0, and solve for s.

   _____

   $s =$ _____ or $s =$ _____

   Which solution makes sense in the problem?

   $s =$ _____

Select the best answer.

3. A seagull is flying upwards at the same time, that a rock is falling off a cliff above the sea.
   h = height in feet above the sea
   t = time in seconds
   Height of the seagull: $h = 3t$
   Height of the rock: $h = -16t^2 + 50$
   Find the approximate time it takes for the rock and the seagull to be at the same height.

   A 1.68 seconds   C 3.36 seconds

   B 3.13 seconds

4. A juggler throws a ball upwards at the same time that an elevator begins climbing a tower at a constant rate of 20 feet per second.
   h = height in feet above the ground
   t = time in seconds
   Height of the ball: $h = -16t^2 + 20t + 5$
   Height of the elevator: $h = 20t$
   Find the approximate time it takes for the ball and the elevator to reach the same height. Round to the nearest hundredth.

   F 0.56 seconds   H 4 seconds

   G 1.12 seconds

Holt McDougal Algebra 1

CHAPTER
8

Quadratic Functions and Equations

Section A Quiz

Select the best answer.

1. Which is a quadratic function?

   A $3x + y^2 = 5$ C $y = 3x + 5$

   B $3x^2 + y = 5$

2. Which function has a graph that opens downward?

   F $-x^2 + y = 0$ H $-y = x^2 + 1$

   G $x^2 - y = 0$

3. What is the vertex of the parabola graphed below?

   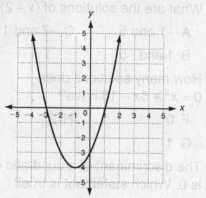

   A (–3, 0)   C (–1, –4)

   B (1, 0)

4. What are the zeros of the function graphed below?

   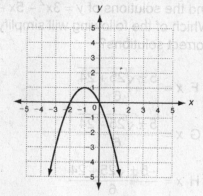

   F –1 and 0   H 0 and 1

   G –2 and 0

5. What is the vertex of the graph of $y = -2x^2 + 8x - 3$?

   A (2, 5)   C (–2, 5)

   B (–2, –27)

6. What function is shown on the graph below?

   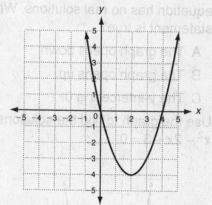

   F $y = -x^2 - 4x$ H $y = -x^2 + 4x$

   G $y = x^2 - 4x$

7. The height in feet of a rocket launched from the ground can be modeled by the function $f(x) = -16x^2 + 96x$, where x is the time in seconds after it is launched. What is the rocket's maximum height?

   A 144 feet   C 288 feet

   B 240 feet

8. Which function's graph has an axis of symmetry of $x = 2$?

   F $y = 3x^2 - 6x + 12$

   G $y = 3x^2 + 12x + 6$

   H $y = -3x^2 + 12x + 6$

9. $f(x) = x^2$ and $g(x) = 3x^2 + 1$. Which statement is true?

   A $g(x)$ is wider than $f(x)$.

   B $g(x)$ is narrower than $f(x)$.

   C $g(x)$ and $f(x)$ have the same vertex.

10. Which function has a vertex different from the vertex of the graph of $f(x) = 2x^2 + 1$?

    F $g(x) = x^2 + 4$ H $g(x) = x^2 + 1$

    G $g(x) = 3x^2 + 1$

CHAPTER
8

Quadratic Functions and Equations

Section B Quiz

Select the best answer.

1. The vertex of a quadratic function is in the second quadrant. The related equation has no real solutions. Which statement is true?

   A The graph opens down.

   B The graph opens up.

   C The y-intercept is 0.

2. Use the graph to find the solutions of $x^2 - 2x - 3 = 0$.

   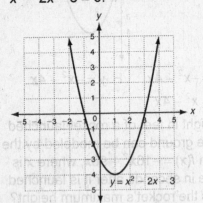

   F −1 and 3   H 1 and −3

   G −1 and −3

3. What are the solutions of $(x + 2)(x - 3) = 0$?

   A 2 and −3   C −2 and 3

   B −2 and −3

4. What are the solutions of $0 = x^2 + 4x - 5$?

   F 4 and −5   H 5 and −1

   G −5 and 1

5. What are the solutions of $0 = 9x^2 - 36$?

   A −6 and 6   C −2 and 2

   B −4 and 4

6. A rectangle with an area of 124 cm² has a length that is 4 times the width. How long is the width? (Round your answer to the nearest tenth.)

   F 5.6 cm   H 22.3 cm

   G 11.1 cm

7. What value of c will make $x^2 - 20x + c$ a perfect square trinomial?

   A −400   C 100

   B −100

8. Solve the system by substitution.

   $$\begin{cases} y = x^2 + 5x + 4 \\ y = 8x + 8 \end{cases}$$

   F (-1, 0), (4, 40)   H (1, 16), (4, 40)

   G (-1, 0), (-4, 0)

9. What are the solutions of $(x - 2)^2 = 9$?

   A −1 and 5   C −7 and 11

   B 1 and −5

10. How many solutions does $0 = x^2 + 5x - 15$ have?

    F 0   H 2

    G 1

11. The discriminant of a quadratic equation is 0. Which statement is true?

    A There are no real solutions.

    B There is one real solution.

    C There are two real solutions.

12. Carlos is using the quadratic formula to find the solutions of $y = 3x^2 - 5x - 2$. Which of the following will simplify to the correct solutions?

    F $x = \dfrac{5 \pm \sqrt{25 + 24}}{6}$

    G $x = \dfrac{5 \pm \sqrt{25 - 24}}{6}$

    H $x = \dfrac{-5 \pm \sqrt{25 + 24}}{6}$

Holt McDougal Algebra 1

CHAPTER
8

Quadratic Functions and Equations
Chapter Test Level A

Select the best answer.

1. Which function is quadratic?

   A $3x - 2y = 5$

   B $5x^2 + x = y - 4$

2. The vertex of this parabola shows that the _____ value of the function is _____.

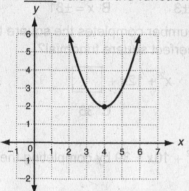

   A maximum, 2   C minimum, 2

   B maximum, 4

3. Which table of values would you use to graph $y = 3x^2$?

   A
x	−2	−1	0	1	2
y	12	3	0	3	12

   B
x	−2	−1	0	1	2
y	36	9	0	9	36

4. Find the zeros of $y = x^2 - 8x + 12$ from its graph below.

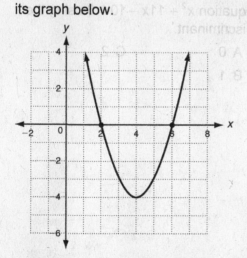

   A −2 and −6   C 2 and 6

   B 0 and 4

5. Find the axis of symmetry of this parabola.

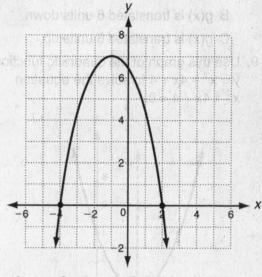

   A $x = -2$ C $x = 1$

   B $x = -1$

6. If you graph $y = x^2 - 6x + 9$, the y-intercept would be _____.

   A −3   B 9

7. The height of a ball in feet is modeled by $f(x) = -16x^2 + 96x$, where x is the time in seconds after it is hit. How long is the ball in the air?

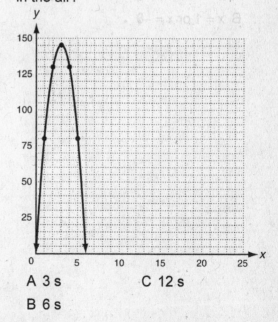

   A 3 s   C 12 s

   B 6 s

Holt McDougal Algebra 1

CHAPTER
8

Quadratic Functions and Equations
Chapter Test Level A continued

8. Compare the graph of $g(x) = x^2 + 6$ with the graph of $f(x) = x^2$.

   A $g(x)$ is narrower.

   B $g(x)$ is translated 6 units down.

   C $g(x)$ is translated 6 units up.

9. Use this graph of the quadratic function $y = x^2 + 4x + 4$ to solve the equation $x^2 + 4x + 4 = 0$.

   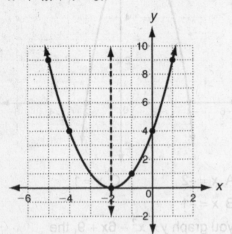

   A $x = -2$

   B $x = -3$ or $x = -1$

   C $x = -4$ or $x = 0$

10. Solve $x^2 - 7x - 8 = 0$ by factoring.

    A $x = -1$ or $x = 8$

    B $x = 1$ or $x = -8$

11. Solve the system by elimination.

    $$\begin{cases} y = x^2 - 1 \\ x - y = -1 \end{cases}$$

    A (-1, 0), (1, 0)   B (-1, 0), (2, 3)

12. Solve $x^2 = 9$ using square roots.

    A $x = \pm 3$ B $x = \pm 81$

13. Which number completes the square to form a perfect square trinomial?

    $$x^2 + 12x + \boxed{}$$

    A 6   C 36

    B 24

14. Solve $x^2 + 10x = 39$ by completing the square.

    A $x = -13$ or $x = 3$

    B $x = -10 + \sqrt{164}$ or $x = -10 - \sqrt{164}$

    C $x = -5 + \sqrt{39}$ or $x = -5 - \sqrt{39}$

15. Solve $2x^2 + 9x + 4 = 0$ using the quadratic formula.

    A $x = -4$ or $x = -\dfrac{1}{2}$

    B $x = \dfrac{-9 \pm \sqrt{113}}{4}$

16. Find the number of real solutions of the equation $x^2 + 11x - 10 = 0$ using the discriminant.

    A 0   C 2

    B 1

LESSON 9-1 Practice A
Geometric Sequences

Find the common ratio of each geometric sequence. Then find the next three terms in each geometric sequence. The first one is done for you.

1. 1, 4, 16, 64, ...

   common ratio: _____**4**_____

   _____**256, 1024, 4096**_____

2. 10, 100, 1000, 10,000, ...

   common ratio: _____

   _____

3. 128, 64, 32, 16, ...

   common ratio: _____

   _____

4. 4, −20, 100, −500, ...

   common ratio: _____

   _____

5. The first term of a geometric sequence is 2 and the common ratio is 4. Find the 6th term.

   _____

6. The first term of a geometric sequence is −3 and the common ratio is 2. Find the 8th term.

   _____

7. The first term of a geometric sequence is 7 and the common ratio is −2. Find the 9th term.

   _____

8. What is the 5th term of the geometric sequence 9, 27, 81, 243, ...?

   common ratio (r): _____

   first term (a_1): _____

   5th term: _____

9. What is the 13th term of the geometric sequence −2, 4, −8, 16, ...?

   common ratio (r): _____

   first term (a_1): _____

   13th term: _____

Holt McDougal Algebra 1

LESSON 9-1 Problem Solving

Geometric Sequences

Write the correct answer.

1. A ball is dropped from 400 feet. The table shows the height of each bounce.

Bounce	Height (ft)
1	280
2	196
3	137.2

Find the height of the ball on the 6th bounce. Round your answer to the nearest tenth of a foot.

Solution:

common ratio: $196 \div 280 = 0.7$

$196 \times 0.7 = 137.2$

$13.7 \times 0.7 = 96.0$

$96.0 \times 0.7 = 67.2$

$67.2 \times 0.7 = 47.1$ feet

2. A plant starts with 1 branch. Every year, each branch becomes 3 branches. A sketch of the plant for the first 3 years is shown. How many branches will the plant have in year 10?

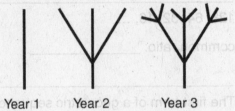

Year 1   Year 2   Year 3

common ratio: 3

_____

How many branches would the plant have in year 10 if the plant had 5 branches the first year? (Each branch still becomes 3 branches every year.)

_____

The table shows the number of houses a builder is putting up. Use the table to answer questions 3–5. Select the best answer.

Month	Houses
1	3
2	6
3	12
4	24

3. The number of houses forms a geometric sequence. What is *r*?

  A 0.5   C 3

  B 2

4. Assuming that the trend continues, how many houses would be in the subdivision in Month 6?

  F 48   H 96

  G 60

5. The builder decides to stop when the total number of houses reaches 48. When will this happen?

  A Month 5   C Month 7

  B Month 6

Practice A
Exponential Functions

1. If a superball is bounced from a height of 20 feet, the function $f(x) = 20(0.9)^x$ gives the height of the ball in feet of each bounce, where x is the bounce number. What will be the height of the 6th bounce? Round your answer to the nearest tenth of a foot. _____
(*Hint:* What is $(0.9)^6$?)

Tell whether each set of ordered pairs satisfies an exponential function. Explain your answer. The first one is done for you.

2. $\{(1,10), (2, 20), (3, 40), (4, 80)\}$ _____ **yes,**

_____ **as the x-values increase by 1, the y-values are multiplied by 2.**

3. $\{(1,5), (2, 10), (3, 15), (4, 20)\}$ _____

_____

Graph each exponential function.

4. $y = 2(3)^x$

x	$y = 2(3)^x$	y	(x, y)
−2	$y = 2(3)^{-2}$	$0.\overline{2}$	$(-2, 0.\overline{2})$
−1	$y = 2(3)^{-1}$	$0.\overline{6}$	$(-1, 0.\overline{6})$
0	$y = 2(3)^0$		
1	$y = 2(3)^1$		
2	$y = 2(3)^2$		

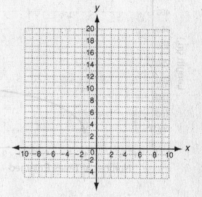

5. $y = -2(4)^x$

x	$y = -2(4)^x$	y	(x, y)
−2			
−1			
0			
1			
2			

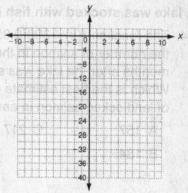

Holt McDougal Algebra 1

LESSON 9-2

Problem Solving

Exponential Functions

Write the correct answer.

1. The function $f(x) = 6(1.5)^x$ models the length of a photograph in inches after the photo has been enlarged by 50% x times.

   a. What is the length of the photograph after it has been enlarged 4 times?

   Solution:

   $6(1.5)^4 = 6(5.0625)$

   $\qquad = 30.375$

   b. Graph the function.

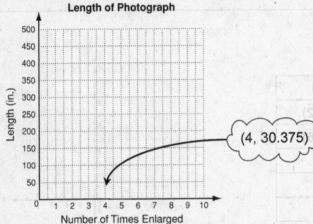

Length of Photograph

Number of Times Enlarged

(4, 30.375)

2. A population of 550 rabbits is increasing by 2.5% each year. The function $y = 5.5 (1.025)^x$ gives the population of rabbits, in hundreds, x years from now. About how long will it take the population to reach 600 rabbits? 1200 rabbits? (*Hint:* $6.0 = 5.5(1.025)^x$)

_____

_____

3. The function $f(x) = 2300(0.995)^x$ shows enrollment in a high school, where x is the number of years after 2005. Use the model to estimate the enrollment in 2013.

_____

_____

A lake was stocked with fish in early April. Select the best answer.

4. The function $f(x) = 300(0.85)^x$ shows the number of salmon in the lake x months after the lake was stocked. Which is the best estimate of the number of landlocked salmon in early July?

   A 157   C 217

   B 184

5. The function $f(x) = 400(1.05)^x$ shows the number of bass x months after the lake was stocked. During what month will the population reach 600?

   F September   H November

   G October   J December

LESSON 9-3

Practice A

Exponential Growth and Decay

Write an exponential growth function to model each situation. Then find the value of the function after the given amount of time. The first one is done for you.

1. Annual sales for a clothing store are $270,000 and are increasing at a rate of 7% per year; 3 years

$y = \boxed{270{,}000}\left(1+\boxed{0.07}\right)^{\boxed{3}}$

$y = \underline{\textbf{\$330,761.61}}$

2. The population of a school is 2200 and is increasing at a rate of 2%; 6 years

$y = \boxed{}\left(1+\boxed{}\right)^{\boxed{}}$

$y \approx \underline{\hspace{3cm}}$

3. The value of a vase is $200 and is increasing at a rate of 8%; 12 years

$y = \underline{\hspace{3cm}}$

$y \approx \underline{\hspace{3cm}}$

Write a compound interest function to model each situation. Then find the balance after the given number of years. The first one is done for you.

4. $20,000 invested at a rate of 3% compounded annually; 8 years.

$A = \boxed{20{,}000}\left(1+\dfrac{\boxed{0.03}}{\boxed{1}}\right)^{\boxed{1}\boxed{8}}$

$A = \boxed{}\left(1+\dfrac{\boxed{}}{\boxed{}}\right)^{\boxed{}\boxed{}}$

5. $35,000 invested at a rate of 6% compounded monthly; 10 years

$A \approx \underline{\hspace{3cm}}$

$A = \underline{\hspace{3cm}}$

6. $35,000 invested at a rate of 8% compounded quarterly; 5 years

$A \approx \underline{\hspace{3cm}}$

Write an exponential decay function to model each situation. Then find the value of the function after the given amount of time. The first one is done for you.

$y = \boxed{800}\left(1-\boxed{0.02}\right)^{\boxed{4}}$

7. The population of a school is 800 and is decreasing at a rate of 2% per year; 4 years

$y \approx \underline{\textbf{738}}$

$y = \boxed{}\left(1-\boxed{}\right)^{\boxed{}}$

8. The bird population in a forest is about 2300 and decreasing at a rate of 4% per year; 10 years

$y \approx \underline{\hspace{3cm}}$

LESSON
9-3

Problem Solving

Exponential Growth and Decay

Write the correct answer.

1. A house was worth $80,000 in 1990. The value of the house increased by an average of 3% each year. Write an exponential growth function to model this situation. Then find the value of the house in 2005.

   Solution:

   $y = 80,000(1.03)^t$

   $y = 80,000(1.03)^{15}$

   $124.637

2. Markiya deposited $500 in a savings account. The annual interest rate is 2%, and the interest is compounded monthly. Write a compound interest function to model this situation. Then find the balance in Markiya's account after 4 years.

   _____

3. The population of a small Midwestern town is 4500. The population is decreasing at a rate of 1.5% per year. Write an exponential decay function to model this situation. Then find the number of people in the town after 25 years.

   _____

   _____

4. Twelve students at a particular high school passed an advanced placement test in 2000. The number of students who passed the test increased by 16.4% each year thereafter. Find the number of students who passed the test in 2004.

   _____

The table below shows the half-lives of several chemical substances. Select the best answer.

5. About how many grams of a 500 g sample of Technetium-99 is left after 2 days?

   A 1.95 g   C 31.25 g

   B 7.81 g

6. Which equation can be used to find how much of a 50 g sample of Nitrogen-16 is left after 7 minutes?

   F $A = 50(0.5)^7$ H $A = 50(0.5)^{60}$

   G $A = 50(0.5)^{42}$

7. How many billions of years will it take 1000 grams of Uranium-238 to decay to just 125 grams?

   A 3   C 13.5

   B 9

Half-Lives	
Nitrogen-16	7 s
Technetium-99	6 h
Sulfur-35	87 days
Tritium	12.3 yr
Uranium-238	4.5 billion yrs

LESSON
9-4

Practice A

Linear, Quadratic, and Exponential Models

Graph each data set. Write *linear*, *quadratic*, or *exponential*.
The first one is done for you.

1. {(0, –4), (1, –2), (2, 0), (3, 2), (4, 4)}

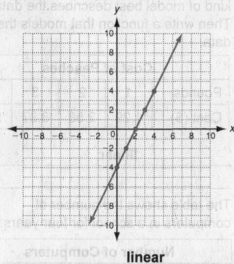

_____linear_____

2. {(–2, –5), (–1, –8), (0, –9), (1, –8), (2, –5)}

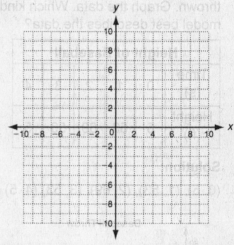

_____

Look for a pattern in each data set. Write *linear*, *quadratic*, or
exponential. The first one is done for you.

3.

x	y
0	3
1	6
2	12
3	24

_____exponential_____

4.

x	y
–2	–10
–1	–8
0	–6
1	–4

_____

5.

x	y
0	2
1	6
2	12
3	20

_____

6. The data in the table show the price of apples at a local store over several years.

Year	1	2	3	4
Cost ($)	0.45	0.90	1.35	1.80

a. Which model best describes the data for apples? _____

b. Write the function that models the data for apples. _____

c. Predict the cost of apples in year 8. _____

LESSON
9-4
Problem Solving
Linear, Quadratic, and Exponential Models

Write the correct answer.

1. The table shows the height of a baseball for different times after it was thrown. Graph the data. Which kind of model best describes the data?

Height of Baseball					
Time (s)	0	1	2	3	4
Height (ft)	5	53	69	53	5

Solution:

(0, 5), (1, 53), (2, 69), (3, 53) (4, 5)

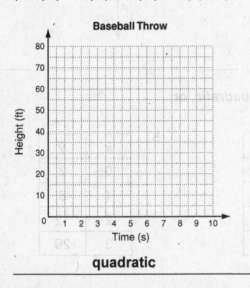

Baseball Throw

_____ **quadratic** _____

2. The table shows the cost of peaches. Look for a pattern and determine which kind of model best describes the data. Then write a function that models the data.

Cost of Peaches				
Pounds	1	2	3	4
Cost ($)	1.29	2.58	3.87	5.16

_____ **linear** _____

_____

3. The table shows the number of computers in a school for four years.

Number of Computers				
Year	'00	'01	'02	'03
Computers	14	28	56	112

Write a function to model the data. Then use the function to predict how many computers the school will have in 2006 if the pattern continues.

_____

The chart shows the ticket sales for movies on two different screens at one theater over four days. Select the best answer.

4. Which kind of model best describes the ticket sales for the movie on screen 1?

  A linear   C exponential

  B quadratic

5. Which function describes the data for screen 1?

  F $y = 40x^2$ H $y = 400x$

  G $y = 40x + 400$

	Screen 1	Screen 2
Day 1	400	3000
Day 2	440	2400
Day 3	480	1920
Day 4	520	1536

6. Which kind of model best describes the ticket sales for the movie on screen 2?

  A linear   C exponential

  B quadratic

Holt McDougal Algebra 1

LESSON **Practice A**
9-5
Nonlinear Systems

Solve by graphing. Use a graphing calculator to check your answers.

1. $\begin{cases} y = x^2 - 2 \\ y = 5x - 8 \end{cases}$

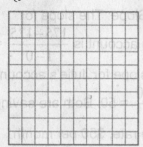

2. $\begin{cases} y = x^2 - 4x + 6 \\ y = -x + 4 \end{cases}$

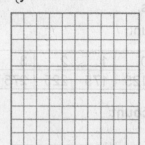

_____

_____

Solve by substitution. Use a graphing calculator to check your answers. The first one is done for you.

3. $\begin{cases} y = x^2 - 3 \\ y = -x + 3 \end{cases}$

4. $\begin{cases} y = x^2 - 2x - 3 \\ y = -2x - 5 \end{cases}$

(−3, 6), (2, 1)

_____

_____

5. $\begin{cases} y = 2x^2 + x - 3 \\ -3x + y = 1 \end{cases}$

6. $\begin{cases} y = x^2 - 25 \\ y = x + 5 \end{cases}$

_____

_____

Solve by elimination. Use a graphing calculator to check your answers. The first one is done for you.

7. $\begin{cases} y = x^2 - 1 \\ 2x - y = -2 \end{cases}$

8. $\begin{cases} y = x^2 + 4x + 3 \\ x - y = -1 \end{cases}$

(−1, 0), (3, 8)

_____

_____

9. $\begin{cases} y = 2x^2 + 4x - 1 \\ 6x + y = -13 \end{cases}$

10. $\begin{cases} y = -x^2 + 3x - 3 \\ 2x - y = 5 \end{cases}$

_____

_____

Holt McDougal Algebra 1

LESSON 9-5

Problem Solving

Comparing Functions

1. George and Julie each deposit money into their savings accounts every month. Compare their accounts by finding slopes and *y*-intercepts.

George's Account

Month	0	1	2	3
Balance ($)	125	175	225	275

Julie's Account

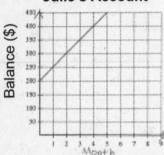

Solution: Slope: The slope for George's account is $\frac{175-125}{1-0}$ = 50. The slope for Julie's account is $\frac{250-200}{1-0}$ = 50. Both are saving at the same rate, $50 per month.

y-intercept: The *y*-intercept for George's account is $125. The *y*-intercept for Julie's account is $200. Julie started with more money than George.

The table and graph below show functions used to model the changing population of the United States. Use the table or graph to select the best answers for questions 2 and 3.

Years since 2000	Population (millions)
0	282
2	288
4	293
6	298
8	304

www.census.gov/popest/geographic/NST-EST2008-01

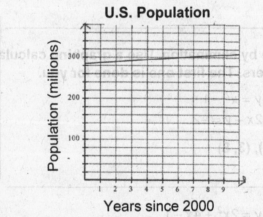

U.S. Population

Years since 2000

2. What is the rate of change in the table from 2000 to 2008?

   A 1.75 million per year

   B 2.75 million per year

   C 22 million per year

3. Which is closest to the rate of change in the graph from 2000 to 2008?

   D about 3.5 million people/year

   E about 3 million people/year

   F about 2.5 million people/year

Holt McDougal Algebra 1

CHAPTER 9 **Exponential Functions**

Section A Quiz

Select the best answer.

1. Which of the following is a geometric sequence?

   A $-1, -3, 9, 27, \ldots$ C $1, 4, 9, 16, \ldots$

   B $-1, 2, -4, 8, \ldots$

2. The first term of a geometric sequence is -2. The common ratio is 4. What is the 6th term?

   F -8192 H 2048

   G -2048

3. Which are the next three terms in the geometric sequence $16, 8, 4, 2, \ldots$?

   A $1, 0, -1$ C $0, -2, -4$

   B $1, \dfrac{1}{2}, \dfrac{1}{4}$

4. Which is the 10th term of the geometric sequence $\dfrac{2}{9}, \dfrac{2}{3}, 2, \ldots$?

   F 6 H $4{,}374$

   G 486

5. Which is the 8th term of the geometric sequence $1024, 256, 64, \ldots$?

   A $\dfrac{1}{8}$ C 1

   B $\dfrac{1}{4}$

6. If a ball is dropped from a height of 18 feet, the function $f(x) = 18(0.75)^x$ gives the height in feet of each bounce, where x is the bounce number. What will be the height of the 7th bounce to the nearest tenth of a foot?

   F 1.8 H 3.2

   G 2.4

7. A population of 200 animals has a growth rate of 1.03% each year. At this growth rate, the function $f(x) = 200(1.03)^x$ gives the population in x years. In how many years will the population first reach 300?

   A 12 C 16

   B 14

8. The graph of which function is shown below?

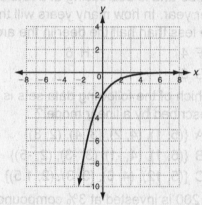

   F $y = -2(2)^x$ H $y = 2(2)^x$

   G $y = -2\left(\dfrac{1}{2}\right)^x$

9. Which of these sets of ordered pairs satisfies an exponential function?

   A $\{(1, -2), (3, -8), (5, -32), (7, -128)\}$

   B $\{(1, -2), (3, 2), (5, 6), (7, 10)\}$

   C $\{(1, -1), (2, -8), (3, -27), (4, -64)\}$

10. The function $f(x) = 4(2)^x$ models the length of an image in centimeters after it has been enlarged by 100% x times. Which of these is the length of the image after it has been enlarged 3 times?

    F 8 centimeters   H 32 centimeters

    G 16 centimeters

CHAPTER 9

Exponential Functions

Section B Quiz

Select the best answer.

1. A population of 100 frogs has a growth rate of 1.25% each month. At this growth rate, the function $f(x) = 100(1.25)^x$ gives the population in x months. In how many months will the population first reach 500?

   A 12   C 8

   B 10

2. The population of deer in an area is 2,000 and is decreasing at a rate of 15% per year. In how many years will there be less than half the deer in the area?

   F 4   H 6

   G 5

3. Which of the following data sets is best described by a linear model?

   A {(5, 1), (4, 2), (3, 4), (2, 8)}

   B {(5, 1), (4, -1), (3, -3), (2, -5)}

   C {(5, 12), (4, 6), (3, 3), (2, 1.5)}

4. $1200 is invested at 3% compounded quarterly. What is the total amount, to the nearest dollar, after 5 years?

   F $1236   H $1393

   G $1245

5. Chess club earnings are $40 per month and will increase at a rate of 2.5% each month. Which function describes this situation?

   A $y = 40(0.75)^x$ C $y = 40(1.025)^x$

   B $y = 40(0.975)^x$ D $y = 40(1.25)^x$

6. Iodine-131 has a half-life of about 8 days. About how much is left from a 50 gram sample after 24 days?

   F 0.781 grams   H 6.250 grams

   G 3.125 grams

7. Which of the following data sets is best described by a quadratic model?

   A {(1, −2), (2, −4), (3, −6), (4, −8)}

   B {(1, −1), (2, 2), (3, −4), (4, 8)}

   C {(1, −1), (2, 2), (3, 7), (4, 14)}

8. The table shows store sales by year. Which function models the data?

Year	0	1	2	3
Sales	5000	4000	3200	2560

   F $y = 5000 + 0.8x$ H $y = 5000(0.8)^x$

   G $y = 5000 + 1.2x$

9. Which kind of model best describes the data graphed below?

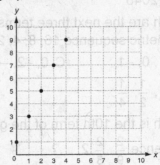

   A linear   C exponential

   B quadratic

10. Argyle has $1000 in his savings account. He wants to save more money. He is looking at two investment plans. Under plan A, he will increase his account balance by $200 a year. Under plan B, he will increase his account balance by 15% each year. How much more will he save with Plan B after 10 years

   F $1,046   H $131

   G $459

11. Which is the average rate of change over the interval [0, 4] for each function?

x	0	2	4	6
f(x)	0	4	16	36

   $g(x) = 2x - 1$

   A $f(x)$: 16, $g(x)$: 8 C $f(x)$: 8, $g(x)$: 16

   B $f(x)$: 4, $g(x)$: 4

Holt McDougal Algebra 1

CHAPTER 9

Exponential Functions

Chapter Test Form A

Select the best answer.

1. Find the next three terms in this sequence: 4, 12, 36, 108, …

   A 180, 252, 324

   B 324, 972, 2916

2. The first term of a geometric sequence is 5 and the common ratio is 2. What is the 4th term of the sequence?

   A 40   C 250

   B 80

3. Which graph shows $y = 2(4)^x$?

   A

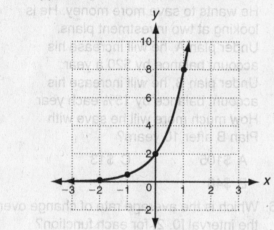

   B

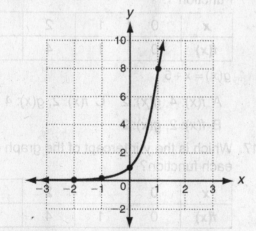

4. The function $f(x) = 10(2)^x$ shows a population after x weeks. To the nearest whole number, what will the population be after 4 weeks?

   A 80   C 20,000

   B 160

5. Which are the next three terms in the geometric sequence 1, 2, 4, 8, …?

   A 12, 24, 48   C 4, 2, 1

   B 16, 32, 64

6. Which is the 10th term of the geometric sequence $\frac{1}{27}, \frac{1}{9}, \frac{1}{3}, 1, …$?

   A 729   C 81

   B 243

7. Which is the 6th term of the geometric sequence 1024, 528, 256,…?

   A 64   C 16

   B 32

8. Which ordered pairs satisfy an exponential function?

   A
x	0	1	2	3
y	0	2	4	6

   B
x	0	1	2	3
y	1	3	9	27

   C
x	0	1	2	3
y	0	1	8	27

Holt McDougal Algebra 1

CHAPTER 9

Exponential Functions

Chapter Test Form A continued

9. Which set of ordered pairs satisfies an exponential function?

A

x	y
–1	1.5
0	3
1	12
2	96

B

x	y
–1	1.5
0	6
1	24
2	96

10. The original value of a sculpture is $950, and the value increases by 15% each year. Find the value of the painting in 8 years.

A $1092.50   C $2906.07

B $2090.00

11. A new play premiers on Saturday, October 1, and 420 people attend. Attendance then decreases by 30% each day. Find the attendance on Tuesday, October 4.

A 144   B 383

12. Determine kind of model best describes this data set.

{(–2, 1), (–1, 3), (0, 5), (1, 7), (2, 9)}

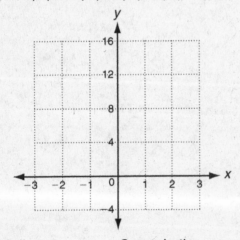

A linear   C quadratic

B exponential

13. Which of the following data sets is best described by a linear model?

A {(2, 4), (3, 9), (4, 16), (5, 25)}

B {(–2, –1), (–3, 0), (–4, 1), (–5, 0)}

C {(2, 12), (3, 6), (4, 0), (5, –6)}

14. Which of the following models best describes the data set?

{(–1, 1), (0, 0), (1, 1), (2, 4)}

A linear   C exponential

B quadratic

15. Ben has $100 in his savings account. He wants to save more money. He is looking at two investment plans. Under plan A, he will increase his account balance by $20 a year. Under plan B, he will increase his account balance by 15% each year. How much more will he save with Plan B after 10 years?

A $105   C $13

B $46

16. Which is the average rate of change over the interval [0, 2] for each function?

Function 1:

x	0	1	2	3
f(x)	0	1	4	9

$g(x) = x + 5$

A f(x): 4, g(x): 2   C f(x): 2, g(x): 4

B f(x): 2, g(x): 2

17. Which is the y-intercept of the graph of each function?

x	0	1	2	3
f(x)	0	1	4	9

$g(x) = x + 5$

A f(x): 0, g(x): 0   C f(x): 5, g(x): 0

B f(x): 0, g(x): 5

LESSON 10-1

Practice A

Organizing and Describing Data

Use the bar graph for Exercises 1–3. The first one is done for you.

1. Which shark lived longer than any other shark?

   Whale Shark
   _____

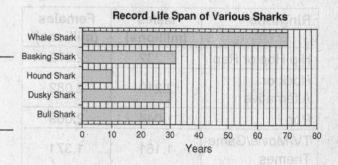

2. About how long did the Basking Shark live?

   _____

3. Which shark lived about one-third as long as the Dusky Shark?

   _____

Use the line graph for Exercises 4–6.

4. In what month was the cost of diesel fuel and regular unleaded the same?

   _____

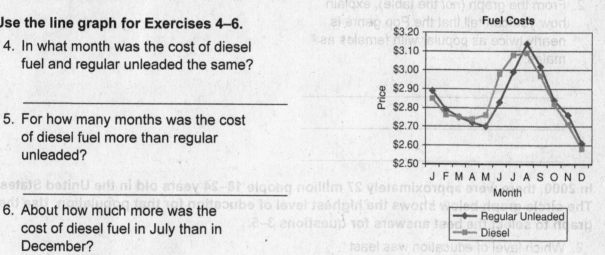

5. For how many months was the cost of diesel fuel more than regular unleaded?

   _____

6. About how much more was the cost of diesel fuel in July than in December?

   _____

7. The table shows what types of pizzas were ordered at Vinnie's Restaurant one weekend. Use the data to make a circle graph. Then tell why a circle graph is appropriate.

Type	Number of Orders
extra cheese	15
pepperoni	55
veggie	30
meat	30
plain	70

Holt McDougal Algebra 1

Name _____ Date _____ Class_____

Problem Solving
Organizing and Describing Data

The table below gives the top five ringtone genres reported during a survey of cell phone subscribers in August, 2005.

Ringtone	Males (millions)	Females (millions)
Hip Hop or Rap	2.232	2.472
Rock or Alternative	2.219	2.082
Pop	1.044	2.069
TV/Movie/Game Themes	1.161	1.371
Classic Rock	0.949	0.918

2. From the graph (*not* the table), explain how you can tell that the Pop genre is nearly twice as popular with females as males.

_____

_____

_____

1. Use the data to make a graph below.

In 2000, there were approximately 27 million people 18–24 years old in the United States. The circle graph below shows the highest level of education for that population. Use the graph to select the best answers for questions 3–5.

3. Which level of education was least represented?

   A Less than high school graduate

   B High school graduate

   C Bachelor's degree or higher

4. How many 18–24 year-olds had a bachelor's degree or higher?

   F 2.16 million   H 10.26 million

   G 8 million

5. How many 18–24 year-olds never attended college?

   A 7.83 million   C 14.58 million

   B 12.42 million

**Education for the Population
18–24 Years Old, 2000**

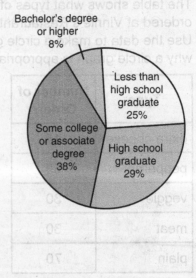

Bachelor's degree or higher 8%

Less than high school graduate 25%

Some college or associate degree 38%

High school graduate 29%

Holt McDougal Algebra 1

LESSON 10-2 Practice A
Frequency and Histograms

1. The number of miles driven by Mrs. Fox each of the 16 days is given. Use the data to make a stem-and-leaf plot with a title and a key. The plot is started for you

Miles Driven							
43	52	98	96	74	32	73	54
57	48	65	78	72	83	54	68

stem	leaves
3	2
4	3 8
5	2 4 4 7

2. The test scores for two Algebra classes are shown in the stem-and-leaf plot.

   a. How many students scored 100? _____2_____

   b. How many students in Period 5 scored greater than 80? _____

   c. What was the lowest score in Period 3? _____

   d. Which Period had more scores?

   How many more? _____

Period 5			stem	Period 3			
4	2	0	0	5	3		
	6	5	2	6	8	9	
7	7	4	2	7	2	9	9
		8	3	8	4	4	4
9	3	1	9	1	3	3	6
			10	0	0		

Key:|6|8 means 68
3|8| means 83

3. The number of calls per day to a fire and rescue service for three weeks is given below. Use the data to complete the frequency table.

Calls for Service										
5	17	2	12	0	6	3	8	15	1	4
19	16	8	2	11	13	18	3	10	6	

Fire and Rescue Service	
Number of Calls	Frequency
0 - 3	6
4 - 7	
8 - 11	
12 - 15	
16 - 19	

4. Use the frequency table in Exercise 3 to make a histogram with a title and axis labels.

5. Which intervals have the same frequency?

_____

Fire and Rescue Service

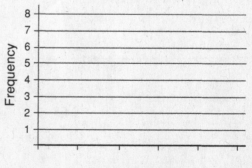

Number of Calls

LESSON 10-2 Problem Solving

Frequency and Histograms

The heights in inches of the 2005 NBA All-Star Game players are given below.

Players' Heights (in.)											
75	78	80	87	72	80	81	83	85	78	76	81
77	78	83	83	78	82	79	80	75	84	82	90

1. Use the data to make a frequency table with intervals. Use an interval of 5.

   Solution:

   Look for the lowest number, 72.

   Look for the highest number, 90.

   Make intervals of 5 starting with the lowest number and ending near the highest. Find how many heights fall in each interval.

Players' Heights	
Heights (in.)	**Frequency**
72–76	4
77–81	11
82–86	7
87–91	2

2. Use your frequency table to make a histogram for the data.

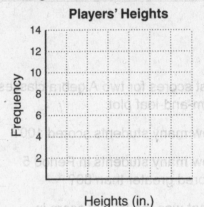

   Players' Heights

   Heights (in.)

Select the best answer.

3. The stem-and-leaf plot to the right gives the MP3 file sizes of the songs on two albums. What is the largest file size for Album 1?

   A 8.9 MB   C 9.9 MB

   B 9.8 MB

MP3 File Sizes (megabytes)

Album 1		Album 2
	0	5	0 1 2 4 5 5 8
6 6 5 3 1	6	0 6 7
7 3 0	7	3 6 8
3 1	8	6
8 7 2 0	9	9

Key: | 8 | 6 *means 8.6 MB*

      1 | 8 | *means 8.1 MB*

LESSON 10-3

Practice A
Data Distributions

Find the mean, median, mode, and range of each data set.
The first one is done for you.

1. 7, 19, 25, 9, 10

   Order the numbers: __7__ , __9__ , __10__ , __19__ , __25__

   mean: $\dfrac{\boxed{7} + \boxed{9} + \boxed{10} + \boxed{19} + \boxed{25}}{\boxed{5}} = 14$ median: __10__

   mode: **none**   range: __25__ – __7__ = __18__

2. 5, 3, 3, 5, 2, 5, 5

   Order the numbers: _____, _____, _____, _____, _____, _____, _____

   mean: _____   median: _____

   mode: _____   range: _____

3. 8, 12, 17, 12, 9, 8

   mean: _____   median: _____

   mode: _____   range: _____

Identify the outlier in each data set, and determine how the outlier affects the mean, median, mode, and range of the data.
The first one is done for you.

4. 7, 11, 29, 3, 10

   outlier: 29, increases mean by 4.25, median
   _____
   by 1.5, and range by 18, no effect on mode

5. 52, 39, 11, 44

6. Mr. Bernard drove 46, 4, 64, 50, and 56 miles on his last five trips. For each question, choose the mean, median, or mode, and give its value.

   a. Which value describes Mr. Bernard's average driving distance? _____

   b. Which value would Mr. Bernard tell his boss to convince him that he spends too much time on the road? Explain.

   _____

7. Use the data to make a box-and-whisker plot. 18, 22, 10, 22, 30, 8, 33, 15, 14

   a. Order the data: _____

   b. Min: _____, Q1 _____, Med: _____,

      Q3: _____, Max: _____

Holt McDougal Algebra 1

LESSON 10-3 Problem Solving

Data Distributions

Write the correct answer.

1. The prices of 5 pairs of shoes were $48, $63, $52, $99, and $58. Find the mean, median, and mode of the prices. Which best represents the typical shoe? Why?

Solution:

mean:

$$\frac{\$48 + \$63 + \$52 + \$99 + \$58}{5} = \$64$$

median: $48, $52, $58, $63, $99

The median is the middle value when the values are in numerical order. The median is $58.

mode: There is no mode because no value occurs more often than the another.

The median represents the typical shoe because only one price is above the mean.

2. The number of cans Xavier recycled each week for eight weeks is 24, 33, 76, 42, 35, 33, 45, and 33. Find the mean, median, and mode of the numbers of cans. How do the mean and median change when the outlier is removed?

mean:

___ + ___ + ___ + ___ + ___ + ___ + ___ + ___ = ___
                    ___

median: ___, ___, ___, ___, ___, ___, ___, ___

The median is the middle value when the values are in numerical order. The median is ___

mode: ___

The number of traffic citations given daily by two police departments over a two-week period is shown in the box-and-whisker plots. Choose the letter of the best answer.

3. What is the best estimate of the difference in the greatest number of citations given by each department in one day?

  A 10

  B 20

  C 30

4. What is the difference in the median number of citations between the two departments?

  F about 8

  G about 15

  H about 22

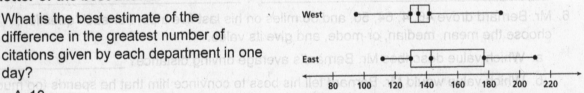

5. Which statement is NOT true?

  A The East department gave the greatest number of citations in one day.

  B The East department gave the least number of citations in one day.

  C The East department has a greater IQR than the West department.

  D The East department has the greater median number of citations in one day.

                               Holt McDougal Algebra 1

LESSON
10-4

Practice A
Misleading Graphs and Statistics

Graph 1

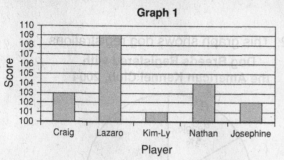

Graph 2

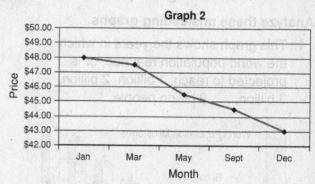

Graph 1 shows the number of points scored by five players in a game.

1. Explain why the graph is misleading. **The vertical *y*-axis does not start at 0. This**

   exaggerates the differences in the scores.

   _____

2. What might someone believe because of the graph? _____

   _____

Graph 2 shows the price change of Product X over one year.

3. Explain why the graph is misleading. _____

   _____

4. What might someone believe because of the graph? _____

   _____

5. Who might want to use this graph? _____

The circle graph shows how Dante spent his allowance.

6. Explain why the graph is misleading.

   _____

7. To whom might Dante show this graph and why?

   _____

   _____

Dante's Spending

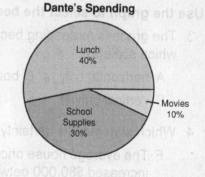

Holt McDougal Algebra 1

LESSON 10-4 Problem Solving

Misleading Graphs and Statistics

Analyze these misleading graphs.

1. This graph shows the years in which the world population reached, or is projected to reach, 1 billion, 2 billion, 3 billion, . . . 9 billion people.

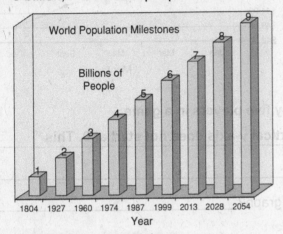

a. Explain why the graph is misleading.

The years
_____
are not at equal time intervals.

b. What might someone believe because of the graph?

that world population
_____
**is increasing in a
linear fashion**

2. This graph shows dog registrations.

**Dog Breeds Registered with
the American Kennel Club, 2004**

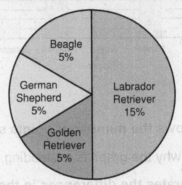

a. Explain why the graph is misleading.

_____

_____

b. Who might want to use this graph, and why?

_____

_____

Use the graph to select the best answer.

3. The graph is misleading because of which scale(s)?

  A horizontal only   C both

  B vertical only

4. Which statement is certainly true?

  F The average house prices have increased $80,000 between 1995 and 2004.

  G The average house price in 2001 was about $160,000.

  H None of the above.

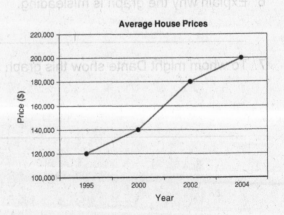

          Holt McDougal Algebra 1

LESSON 10-5

Practice A

Experimental Probability

Identify the sample space and the outcome shown for each experiment.

1. rolling a number cube

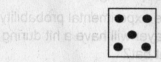

       sample space: {1, 2, 3, 4, 5, 6};

           outcome {5}

2. spinning a spinner

_____

_____

**Write *impossible, unlikely, as likely as not, likely*, or *certain*
to describe each event.**

3. Selecting a green marble from a bag of white marbles _____

4. Choosing a vowel from the letters A, M, O, F, P, I _____

5. Correctly guessing a number between 1 and 3 when
you have 2 tries

_____

**An experiment consists of randomly choosing a
colored card from a box. Use the results in the table
to find the experimental probability of each event.**

Outcome	Frequency
red card	7
yellow card	12
orange card	8
white card	13

6. choosing a yellow card _____

7. choosing an orange card _____

8. not choosing a white card _____

9. A cook inspects 20 hamburgers and finds 3 of them are missing a pickle.

a. What is the experimental probability that a hamburger will
be missing a pickle? _____

b. The restaurant makes 300 hamburgers. Predict the number
of hamburgers that are likely to be missing a pickle. _____

Holt McDougal Algebra 1

Problem Solving

LESSON 10-5

Experimental Probability

Write the correct answer.

1. Bottled juices have prizes printed on the inside of the bottle caps. 2 million caps say "Sorry"; 1.5 million say "Free Bottle"; 0.4 million say "T-Shirt"; and 0.1 million say "CD."

   a. Identify the sample space.

   Solution:

   What are the possible outcomes if you buy a bottled juice?

   Sorry, Free Bottle, T-Shirt, CD

   b. If Tammy buys one bottle, is it impossible, unlikely, as likely as not, likely, or certain that she will get a cap that says "Sorry"?

   _____

2. A baseball player had 1408 hits out of 5271 times at bat during his entire career.

   a. What is the experimental probability that the player will have a hit during any time at bat?

   _____

   b. If the player has 570 at-bats during a season, predict the number of hits he will have during the season.

   _____

A drug company tests the effectiveness of a diabetes test by giving it to several people who actually know whether or not they have diabetes. The results are in the table below. Select the best answer.

3. What is the experimental probability that this test will *not* identify someone who actually does have diabetes?

   A 2.9 %   C 20%

   B 16.6%

4. If this test is used on 1000 patients who do not know whether or not they have diabetes, about how many patients would the test predict *do* have diabetes?

   F 66   H 92

   G 79

	Volunteer _____ have diabetes.	
	does	does not
Test predicts that the person **have diabetes.** does	10	4
does not	2	136

Holt McDougal Algebra 1

LESSON 10-6

Practice A
Theoretical Probability

Find the theoretical probability of each outcome.
The first one is done for you.

1. flipping one coin and having it land tails up   **50%**

2. randomly choosing a yellow marble from a bag of 3 yellow marbles and 7 blue marbles   _____

3. rolling a 1 on a number cube   _____

4. randomly choosing the letter A from the letters in MATH _____

5. The probability it will rain is 10%. What is the probability it will not rain?   _____

6. The probability of choosing a red marble from a bag is $\frac{3}{4}$.

   What is the probability of **not** choosing a red marble?   _____

7. A spinner has red, green, and blue. The probability of spinning red is 0.2 and the probability of spinning blue is 0.3. What is the probability of spinning a green?   _____

8. The probability of winning first place in a contest is 5%. What is the probability of not winning first place?   _____

9. The odds in favor of winning a contest are 1:4.

   a. What is the total number of possible outcomes?   _____

   b. How many ways can a person win?   _____

   c. What is the probability that a person wins?   probability = ▯/▯

10. The odds against a spinner landing on green are 7:2.

    a. What is the total number of possible outcomes?   _____

    b. How many ways can the spinner **not** land on green?   _____

    c. What is the probability of the spinner not landing on green?   probability = ▯/▯

11. The table shows how many of each letter are in a bag. Find the following.

    a. *P*(A) _____   b. *P*(not B) _____

    c. odds in favor of C _____

Letter	How Many in Bag
A	6
B	4
C	5

Holt McDougal Algebra 1

LESSON 10-6 Problem Solving

Theoretical Probability

A game is played with tiles. Each tile has numbers, pictures, or characters on it. Most of the tiles can be grouped into suits. From a certain set of tiles, the odds *in favor* of selecting a tile from the bamboo suit is 1:3. The first one is done for you.

1. What is the probability of selecting a tile from the bamboo suit?

$$\frac{1}{4}$$

2. What is the probability of selecting a tile that is *not* from the bamboo suit?

_____

3. Any set of game tiles has 36 tiles in the bamboo suit. How many tiles are in the entire set? (*Hint:* Set up a proportion using your answer from question 1.)

_____

You drop a ball into the top of the machine shown below. As the ball falls, it goes either left or right as it hits each peg. In total, the ball can follow 16 different paths. (See if you can draw all 16 paths.) The ball eventually lands in one of the bins at the bottom and you win that amount of money. (One path to $0 is shown.) Select the best answer.

4. What is the probability of winning $2? (*Hint:* How many paths out of 16 lead to $2?)

   A $\frac{1}{16}$ C $\frac{1}{4}$

   B $\frac{1}{8}$

5. What is the probability of winning $1?

   F $\frac{3}{16}$ H $\frac{3}{8}$

   G $\frac{1}{4}$

6. What are the odds in favor of winning nothing ($0)?

   A 1:1   C 1:3

   B 1:2

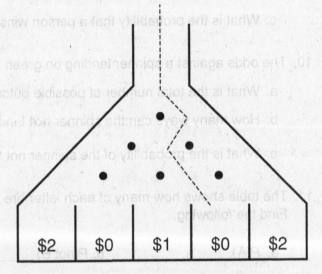

     Holt McDougal Algebra 1

LESSON 10-7

Practice A
Independent and Dependent Events

Tell whether each set of events is independent or dependent. Explain your answer. The first one is done for you.

1. You roll a number cube three times. **independent; the outcome of one roll**

   does not affect the other rolls.

2. Select a marble from a bag, do not replace it, then select another marble. _____

   _____

3. **A number cube is rolled two times.**

   a. Are the events independent or dependent? _____

   b. What is the probability of rolling a 5 both times? _____

4. **The numbers 1 – 20 are written on pieces of paper and put in a box. Two pieces of paper are randomly selected and not replaced.**

   a. Are the events independent or dependent? _____

   b. What is the probability of selecting a number less than 6 both times? _____

5. **A bag contains 1 red, 7 black, and 2 yellow marbles. State whether the following events are independent or dependent. Then find the probabilities.**

   a. probability of selecting a black marble, replacing it, then selecting a red marble

   _____

   b. probability of selecting a yellow marble, **not** replacing it, then selecting another yellow marble?

   _____

   c. probability of selecting 1 yellow marble, **not** replacing it, then selecting a black marble

   _____

The number of drama club members per grade is given. Two members will be chosen for a trip.

	Drama Club
9th	8
10th	2

6. What is the probability both members are 9th graders? _____

   (*Hint:* $\frac{8}{10} \times \frac{7}{9}$)

7. What is the probability both members are 10th graders? _____

Problem Solving
Independent and Dependent Events

Janeesa's backpack has 4 pens and 6 pencils in the front pocket. She reaches in, grabs one, and removes it. Then she reaches in again, grabs another, and removes it. Write the correct answer. The first one is done for you

1. Are these two events independent or dependent? Explain.

     dependent; the item removed

     first affects the sample space

     for the second item.

2. What is the probability that Janeesa removes two pens?

     _____

3. What is the probability that Janeesa removes two pencils?

     $$\frac{6}{10} \times \frac{5}{9} =$$

4. What is the probability that Janeesa removes a pencil and then a pen?

     _____

5. What is the probability that she removes a pen and then a pencil? (*Hint:* see question 4.)

     _____

On a game show, a person tries to win a car by randomly picking tiles from a bag. Some of the tiles are printed with the digits in the price of the car and some are printed with strikes (red X's). Select the best answer.

6. The game is played with 7 tiles—4 digits and 3 strikes. Whenever you pick a strike, it is removed from the bag. In this game, what is the probability of picking three strikes in a row?

     A $\frac{1}{343}$ C $\frac{1}{35}$

     B $\frac{6}{343}$

7. A new game uses 6 tiles—5 digits and 1 strike. Whenever you pick a strike, it is put back in the bag. In this game, what is the probability of picking three strikes in a row?

     F $\frac{1}{216}$ H $\frac{1}{36}$

     G $\frac{1}{120}$

Holt McDougal Algebra 1

CHAPTER
10
Data Analysis and Probability
Section A Quiz

Select the best answer.

1. Which type of graph would best show the change in the number of student absences over the school year?

   A circle   C bar

   B line

Use the double-bar graph for 2–3.

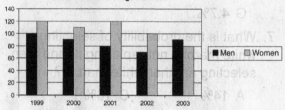
Enrollment in College Courses

2. How many people were enrolled in college courses in 1999?

   F 100   H 220

   G 120

3. In what year was the difference between men's and women's enrollment the greatest?

   A 2000   C 2002

   B 2001

Use the stem-and-leaf plot for 4–6.

```
 7 | 2  2  2  3
 8 | 0  5  8
 9 | 3  7        Key: 8|0 = 80
10 | 0
```

4. If you organized the data in a frequency table, which *could* be intervals?

   F 70–80 and 80–90

   G 70–79 and 80–84

   H 70–79 and 80–89

5. What is the median?

   A 72   C 82.5

   B 80

6. What is the mean?

   F 72   H 83.2

   G 82.5

7. For the set {1, 1, 2, 4, 5, 6, 7, 8, 10,} which would NOT be affected if another value of 10 was included?

   A range   C median

   B mean

8. Look at the box-and-whisker plot below. Between what values does the middle half of the data fall?

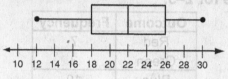

   F 12 and 18   H 18 and 26

   G 12 and 30

9. One type of car gets 70 mi/gal and 4 other cars get 30 mi/gal. Why is this misleading: "The average mi/gal for these 5 cars is 38"?

   A The sample is biased.

   B The median is equal to the mode.

   C The mean is not a good descriptor for this data set.

10. What might someone be incorrectly influenced to believe based on the graph below?

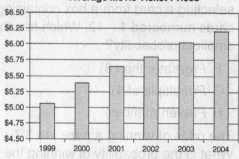
Average Movie Ticket Prices

   F Prices have been increasing.

   G Prices have been decreasing.

   H Prices tripled between 1999 and 2004.

CHAPTER 10

Data Analysis and Probability

Section B Quiz

Select the best answer.

1. Of 98 cell phones 2 are not working. If a company has 850 of the phones, how many are likely to not be working?

   A 2   C 17

   B 9

An experiment consists of spinning a spinner. Use the results in the table for 2–3.

Outcome	Frequency
Red	7
Green	3
Blue	10

2. What is the probability of spinning green?

   F $\frac{3}{20}$ H $\frac{7}{20}$

   G $\frac{3}{10}$

3. What is the probability of NOT spinning red?

   A $\frac{7}{10}$ C $\frac{13}{20}$

   B $\frac{7}{20}$

4. An experiment consists of randomly selecting a card from a box containing cards numbered 1 – 12. Which has the smallest probability?

   F P(greater than 8)

   G P(multiple of 4)

   H P(even number)

5. The odds of winning a prize are 3:7. What is the probability of winning the prize?

   A $\frac{3}{10}$ C $\frac{7}{10}$

   B $\frac{3}{7}$

A bag contains 4 red, 2 blue, 6 green and 8 white marbles. Use this to answer questions 6–7. Round answers to nearest tenth.

6. What is the probability of selecting a green marble, replacing it, and then selecting a red marble?

   F 4.5%   H 6.0%

   G 4.7%

7. What is the probability of selecting a white marble, not replacing it, and then selecting another white marble?

   A 14%   C 16%

   B 14.7%

8. Which are independent events?

   F Two volunteers are chosen from a group.

   G Two marbles are selected without replacing the first.

   H Two coins are tossed.

9. Which if these is the probability of rolling a 1 or a 6?

   A $\frac{1}{6}$ C $\frac{1}{3}$

   B $\frac{1}{5}$

10. Which of these is the probability of rolling two even numbers in a row?

    F 1   H $\frac{1}{4}$

    G $\frac{1}{2}$

11. Which are dependent events?

    A Two coins are tossed.

    B One card is drawn, replaced, and then another card is drawn.

    C Two people are selected from a group.

Data Analysis and Probability

CHAPTER 10

Chapter Test Form A

Select the best answer.

1. Use this bar graph of marbles to fiind how many more marbles are blue than red.

Marble Colors in One Bag

A 3

B 6

C 9

2. Which type of graph would be best for displaying this data?

Board Members' Opinions About Restoring Town Hall

Opinion	Board members
In Favor	18
Oppose	10
Undecided	2

A circle graph

B line graph

3. This stem-and-leaf plot gives the number of items correct on a test for ten students. Which data set is plotted?

Stem	Leaves
3	5 6 9
4	2 3 5 5 8
5	0 0

A {5, 5, 24, 34, 53, 54, 54, 63, 84, 93}

B {35, 36, 39, 42, 43, 45, 45, 48, 50, 50}

The high temperatures for Concord, CA, for October 1–15, 2005, are given below. Use this data for questions 4–7.

High Temperatures (°F)
80 73 72 76 84 86 82 73
81 84 78 85 87 84 70

4. Which frequency table reflects the data?

A

Temp (°F)	Freq.
70–74	4
75–79	2
80–84	3
85–89	6

B

Temp (°F)	Freq.
70–74	4
75–79	2
80–84	6
85–89	3

5. What is wrong with this histogram?

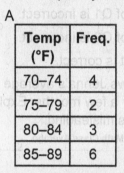

Low Temperatures for Oct. 1–15, 2005

A The bar for 74–77 is too short.

B The bar for 78–81 is too tall.

C The bar for 82–85 is too tall.

6. Find the mean, median, and mode. (Round answers to the nearest tenth.)

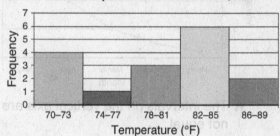

	mean	median	mode
A	79.5	80.5	no mode
B	79.7	81	84
C	79.7	81	no mode

CHAPTER 10

Data Analysis and Probability
Chapter Test Form A continued

7. What, if anything, is wrong with this box-and-whisker plot?

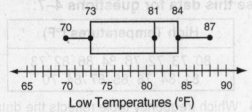

Low Temperatures (°F)

A The value of Q1 is incorrect.

B The value of Q3 is incorrect.

C The boxplot is correct.

8. This graph shows Jenna's average in math class over a few months. Explain why the graph is misleading.

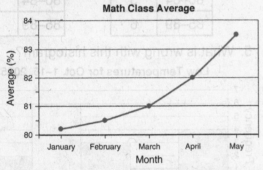

A The intervals on the vertical axis are not equal.

B The scale on the vertical axis does not begin at zero.

A company inspects 50 computers and finds that 45 have no defects. Use this information for questions 9 and 10.

9. What is the experimental probability that a computer chosen at random has no defects?

 A 5%   C 90%

 B 45%

10. If the company sells 20,000 computers, predict the number that have no defects.

 A 1000   C 18,000

 B 9000

11. Find the theoretical probability of rolling a number greater than 4 on a number cube.

 A $\frac{1}{3}$

 B $\frac{1}{2}$

12. The probability of picking a red marble from a bag is $\frac{1}{5}$. What are the odds in favor of picking a red marble?

 A 1:4

 B 1:6

13. A number cube is rolled 2 times in a row. What is the probability of rolling a 3 both times?

 A $\frac{1}{36}$ C $\frac{1}{3}$

 B $\frac{1}{30}$

14. A bag has 10 marbles, and 4 are black. Joseph picks 2 marbles without replacing the first. What is the probability that both are black?

 A $\frac{3}{25}$

 B $\frac{2}{15}$

 C $\frac{4}{25}$

15. Which are independent events?

 A Two juniors are chosen for a school play.

 B A coin is tossed and a number cube is rolled.

 C 12 people are chosen to take a survey.

Holt McDougal Algebra 1

End of Course Assessment

Select the best answer.

1. Which situation is best modeled by the expression $2 + x$?

   A Tabitha lost 2 of her x marbles under the couch.

   B Sudhir had $2 and spent x dollars on a hamburger.

   C Fatima is 2 years older than her sister Delilah who is x years old.

2. Solve $8x - (2x + 3) = 4x + 1$.

   F $-\dfrac{1}{3}$ H 2

   G -1

3. Which expression represents the perimeter of the triangle below?

   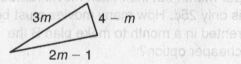

   A $3 + 4m$ C $5 + 4m$

   B $3 + 6m$

4. If $x = -1$, which quadrant does the point $(2x, -x)$ lie in?

   F Quadrant I   H Quadrant IV

   G Quadrant II

5. The time it takes Jarvis to get to school on his bike is $\dfrac{1}{3}$ of the time it takes to walk. Which equation can be solved to find the time it takes Jarvis to walk to school if he can bike there in 5 minutes?

   A $3w = 5$ C $\dfrac{1}{3}w = 5$

   B $w = \dfrac{1}{3} \cdot 5$

6. Solve $-\dfrac{x}{7} - \dfrac{2}{3} = \dfrac{4}{21}$.

   F -6 H 6

   G $-1\dfrac{1}{3}$

7. Approximately 9 out of 100 people are left handed. Out of a population of 1740 people, how many are likely to be left handed?

   A 139   C 174

   B 157

8. Solve $2\,|x + 1| = 8$.

   F 3   H $-5, 3$

   G 3, 5

9. Which is NOT a solution to the inequality $4x - 7 < 5$?

   A -2 C 3

   B 1

10. Which inequality has the solutions graphed below?

    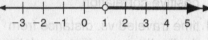

    F $2x + 7 < 9$ H $2x + 7 \geq 9$

    G $2x + 7 > 9$

11. Lorena and Sebastian are both 5 years old. Every year they each get a cash present. Sebastian gets $1.50 for every year in his age, and Lorena gets $20. How old will they be when Sebastian gets more money than Lorena?

    A 9   C 14

    B 13

12. Which of the following statements is true?

    F The dependent variable determines the domain of the function.

    G In $y = 2x + 1$, x is the dependent variable.

    H In $y = 2x + 1$, y is the dependent variable.

13. Which function has $(0, 7)$ on its graph?

    A $-3x + y = 7$ C $y = 14 - x$

    B $y = x - 7$

14. Which situation best fits the graph below and what type of correlation is it?

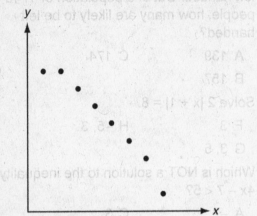

  F distance traveled vs. cost of gas; negative correlation

  G distance traveled vs. cost of gas; positive correlation

  H time traveled vs. distance from destination; negative correlation

15. A function has x-intercept 3 and y-intercept 2. Which of the functions below could be this function?

  A $4 + 3x = 2y$

  B $2y + 3x = 4$

  C $3y - 6 = -2x$

16. The scoring for a football game by quarters was recorded as the ordered pairs {(1, 7), (2, 10), (3, 21), (4, 21)}. Which of the following statements is true?

  F The relation is a function with domain {1, 2, 3, 4}.

  G The relation is a function with domain {7, 10, 21}.

  H The relation is not a function.

17. Which equation describes a line that passes through (7, 1) and is perpendicular to the line described by $y = \frac{1}{2}x + 3$?

  A $y = 2x - 13$ C $y = 2x - 6$

  B $y = 2x - 7$

18. The change from $f(x) = 4x + 2$ to $g(x) = 3x + 2$ is an example of which type of transformation?

  F rotation   H translation up

  G reflection

19. A video store has two renting plans. Plan A charges a $10 monthly fee and $2 for every movie rented. Plan B charges $40 per month but then each movie rented is only 25¢. How many movies must be rented in a month to make plan B the cheaper option?

  A 17   C 28

  B 18

20. Classify the system $\begin{cases} y = 2x + 3 \\ y = -2x + 3 \end{cases}$.

  F inconsistent and independent

  G consistent and independent

  H consistent and dependent

21. Which point is a solution of $\begin{cases} y - 3x \geq 2 \\ y \leq x + 9 \end{cases}$?

  A (-2, 8)   C (4, -1)

  B (-1, 4)

End of Course Assessment

22. Which of the following pairs of points is the solution to the system of equations below?

$$\begin{cases} y = x^2 - 1 \\ y = -x + 5 \end{cases}$$

F (2, 3), (4, 15) H (−3, 8), (2, 3)

G (−3, 8), (1, 4)

23. Which of the following is NOT equivalent to $\left(\dfrac{x^2 y}{4x^5}\right)^{-2}$

A $\left(\dfrac{y}{4x^3}\right)^{-2}$ C $\left(\dfrac{16x^5}{y^2}\right)$

B $\left(\dfrac{4x^3}{y}\right)^2$

24. Identify the quartic trinomial.

F $4x^4 - 2x^5 + 6x$

G $x^3 + 14x^4 - 3$

H $4x^4 - x^3 - 5x + 1$

25. What is the volume of the rectangular prism shown below?

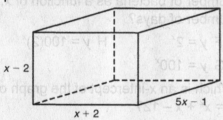

A $5x^3 - 21x^2 + 24x - 4$

B $5x^3 - x^2 - 20x + 4$

C $5x^3 + x^2 - 20x - 4$

26. Which is the prime factorization of 540?

F $3 \cdot 4 \cdot 5 \cdot 9$ H $2^2 \cdot 3^3 \cdot 5$

G $2^2 \cdot 3 \cdot 5 \cdot 9$

27. Which pair of terms has a GCF of 5x?

A $5x^2$ and 15   C $25x^2$ and $50x$

B $5x^2$ and $20x$

28. Factor $2x^2 + 17x + 30$.

F (2x + 6) (x + 5)

G (2x + 5) (x + 6)

H (2x + 10) (x + 3)

29. Which values of b and c would make $x^2 + bx + c$ a perfect square trinomial?

A b = 2, c = 6   C b = 8, c = 16

B b = 6, c = 12

30. Which of the following statements does NOT apply to the quadratic function $f(x) = -x^2 + 7$?

F The vertex is at (0, 7).

G The parabola opens downward.

H Its axis of symmetry is y = 0.

31. Some mountains resemble parabolas. If the following functions describe shapes of mountains, which of the following mountains would have the steepest slope?

A Mountain A: $y = -\dfrac{3}{2}x^2 + 5$

B Mountain B: $y = -x^2 + 5$

C Mountain C: $y = -\dfrac{1}{2}x^2 + 5$

32. Solve $x^2 + 10x = 39$ by completing the square.

F $x = -5 \pm \sqrt{14}$

G x = −3 or 13

H x = 3 or −13

End of Course Assessment

33. If a total of 28 students were surveyed, to help figure out what color their school banner should be, how many chose green?

School Banner

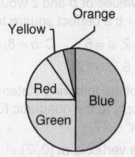

A 4 students   C 7 students

B 6 students

34. Which of the following pieces of information can be obtained from a box-and-whisker plot?

F the mean of the data set

G the number of values in the data set

H the median of the data set

35. Ivan has 7 tickets to a concert and 2 of the tickets have backstage passes. If Ivan passes out the tickets randomly to 7 friends, what are the odds against his friend Jada getting a backstage pass?

A 2:5   C 5:2

B 2:7

36. The table shows the number of customers at an ice cream shop and the number of sundaes sold. Which is the best line of fit for the data?

Customers	10	12	20	24
Sundaes	60	70	118	148

F $y \approx 6.24x - 4.0$ H $y \approx 6.82x - 11.0$

G $y \approx 6.0x - 1.3$

37. What is the 5th term in the geometric sequence 96, 72, 54,...?

A 30   C 36

B $30\frac{3}{8}$

38. Which two quadrants is the function $f(x) = 2(4)^x$ graphed in?

F Quadrants I and II

G Quadrants II and III

H Quadrants III and IV

39. Which function has the higher rate of change over the interval [0, 3]?

A $y = 2x + 4$ C $y = 2(3)^x$

B $y = -x - 3$

40. Which is the most precise measurement?

F 84.2 cm   H 842 mm

G 84 cm

41. What is the x-value for the solution to the system of equations below?

$$\begin{cases} 2x + y = 8 \\ -4x - y = -14 \end{cases}$$

A −3   C 3

B −2

42. A research biologist starts with 100 bacteria. The number of bacteria doubles each day. Which equation gives the number of bacteria as a function of x, the number of days?

F $y = 2^x$ H $y = 100(2)^x$

G $y = 100^x$

43. Which is an x-intercept of the graph of $y = x^2 + x - 12$?

A 1   C −3

B −4

    Holt McDougal Algebra 1

Answer Key Equations

1-1 VARIABLES AND EXPRESSIONS

Practice A

2. y less than 5

3. the quotient of n and 4

4. 10 increased by t

5. the product of 3 and s

6. $c + 2$ 7. $5m$

8. 8   9. 4

10. 3   11. 16

12. 8

13. a. $j - 4$

    b. 11 years old; 16 years old; 54 years old

Problem Solving

2. $5.15 - w$

3. C   4. F

5. B

1-2 SOLVING EQUATIONS BY ADDING AND SUBTRACTING

Practice A

2. $+9; +9; t = 23$ 3. $+6; +6; p = 4$

4. $-; -4$ 5. $-6; -6; p = 4$

6. $-21; -21; x = 4$

7. $x + 18 = 86$; $x = 68$; The score on the second test was higher than the first, so the score on the first test should be less than 86.

8. $x - 4 = 29$; 33°F; The actual temperature was lower than expected, so the expected temperature should be greater than 29°F.

Problem Solving

2. 184; 23; 23; 23; 207

3. A   4. F

5. B   6. G

1-3 SOLVING EQUATIONS BY MULTIPLYING AND DIVIDING

Practice A

2. -3×7; $n = -21$ 3. -3×5; $t = -15$

5. $p = 10$ 6. $m = 1$

7. $\frac{x}{4} = 63$; 252 students

8. $4s = 64$; 16 mm

Problem Solving

2. 10; 10; 2.5

3. A   4. H

5. B

1-4 SOLVING TWO-STEP AND MULTI-STEP EQUATIONS

Practice A

1. 2; 10; 2   2. 3; 8; 4

3. 21; 9; 3   5. $x = 5.4$

6. $r = -23$ 7. $y = 3$

8. $b = 24$ 9. $y = -3$

10. $7x + 6 + 5x$ 11. 12; +6

12. $12x$; 84   13. x; 7

14. 55°; 35°

Problem Solving

2. $4p$; 4; 4; 2.9   3. C

4. F   5. B

1-5 SOLVING EQUATIONS WITH VARIABLES ON BOTH SIDES

Practice A

1. $2a$; 3; 10; 5   2. $4r$; 9; -4

3. $-5b$; 30; $5b$; $3b$; 10

4. 6; $c - 13$; $c = -19$

5. 2; $x = 3$

6. a. $8 + 2h = 2 + 5h$

    b. 2 hours

    c. $12

Holt McDougal Algebra 1

Problem Solving

2. −1200; 2030; 290d; 7

3. B   4. G

5. C

1-6 SOLVING FOR A VARIABLE

Practice A

1. $K - 273 = C$ 2. 1; $f = \dfrac{1}{T}$

3. $y = \dfrac{x}{5}$ 4. $w = \dfrac{v}{9}$

5. $s = r - 4t$

6. a. $F = 2 + E - V$ 7. a. $t = \dfrac{d}{r}$

   b. 6 faces   b. 3 hours

Problem Solving

1. $r = \dfrac{d}{t}$ 2. 9.1 m/s

3. 13.00; 110; 8.5; 8.5 m/s

4. A   5. H

1-7 SOLVING ABSOLUTE-VALUE EQUATIONS

Practice

1. 2

2. Case 1: −7; 4; 4; −11; Case 2: 7; 4; 4; 3

3. 6; Case 1: −6; −5; Case 2: 6; 7

5. {−14, 14}   6. {−17, 17}

7. {−11, 7}   8. {−5, 5}

9. {−7, 3}

11. minimum: 22 mi/gal; maximum: 26 mi/gal

Problem Solving

2. 0.021; 53.021; 53; 52.979

3. B   4. B

5. C

1-8 RATES, RATIOS, AND PROPORTIONS

Practice A

1. 20   2. 58 ft/s

3. $1.05/lb   4. 8; 2; $y = 4$

5. 6; 3; $x = 18$ 6. 25; m; $m = 2$

7. 150 in.   8. 160 mi

Problem Solving

1. 2.67 rolls/minute

2. 60; 300; 300; 0.53; 0.53 mi/min

3. C   4. G

5. C

1-9 APPLICATIONS OF PROPORTIONS

Practice A

1. 4   2. 28

3. width = 4 cm; length = 12 cm

4. $\dfrac{6}{12}$ or $\dfrac{2}{4}$ or $\dfrac{1}{2}$

5. 16 cm; 32 cm

   12 cm^2; 48 cm^2

6. $\dfrac{16}{32}$ or $\dfrac{1}{2}$

7. $\dfrac{12}{48}$ or $\dfrac{1}{4}$

Problem Solving

2. cube; 2; 2; $3 \times 3 \times 3$; 8

3. B   4. H

5. B   6. G

1-10 PRECISION AND ACCURACY

Practice A

1. 3215 g   2. 48 in.

3. 3.82 cm   4. 81 oz

5. 3002 mL   6. 421 cm

7. 4 qt   8. 2.9 ft

9. 25 oz   10. 5285 ft

11. 3810 mm   12. 12,000 lb

13. 19.6 lb–20.4 lb

14. 28.8 cm–31.2 cm   15. 94.8 ft–105.2 ft

16. 57.3 m–62.7 m

17. 75.2° F–84.8° F   18. 17.1 L–18.9 L

Holt McDougal Algebra 1

19. 7.2 kg–8.8 kg

20. 18.4° C–21.6° C   21. 3.4 mL–3.6 mL

22. 33.6 km–46.4 km

23. 34.2 in.–37.8 in.

24. 78.9 mg–82.1 mg

Problem Solving

1. No; it is too long

2. 1, 4, 5   3. C

4. G   5. B

6. G

Equations Section A Quiz

1. C   2. F

3. B   4. H

5. C   6. H

7. B   8. G

9. A   10. G

11. C   12. G

13. B   14. H

Equations Section B Quiz

1. C   2. F

3. C   4. H

5. B   6. G

7. B   8. H

9. B   10. F

Equations Chapter 1 Test

1. A   2. A

3. B   4. B

5. A   6. B

7. A   8. C

9. B   10. B

11. A   12. B

13. C   14. B

15. A   16. A

17. B   18. B

19. B   20. A

21. A   22. A

23. C   24. A

25. C   26. C

Holt McDougal Algebra 1

Answer Key Inequalities

2-1 GRAPHING AND WRITING INEQUALITIES

Practice A

2. a

3. b

4. d

5.

6.

7.

8.

10. b

11. a

12. c

13. h = height; $h > 4$;

Problem Solving

2. weight; 2,500

3. f = percent forested; $f \le 30$

4. w = weight; $w \ge 125$

5. B

6. G

7. A

2-2 SOLVING INEQUALITIES BY ADDING OR SUBTRACTING

Practice A

1. $t > 8$

2. $p \ge 5$

3. $m < -9$

4. $w \le 3$

5. $g > 0$

6. $32 + d \ge 40$; $d \ge 8$

7. $17 + h > 30$; $h > 13$

Problem Solving

2. q; $q + 9$; q; 11

3. A

4. H

5. C

2-3 SOLVING INEQUALITIES BY MULTIPLYING OR DIVIDING

Practice A

1. $x \ge 3$

2. $a < 5$

3. $b > 4$

4. $y \le -2$

5. $x > -4$

6. $k < -3$

7. $n \le 6$

8. $x \ge 0$

Holt McDougal Algebra 1

9. $2b \le 15$; $b \le 7.5$; 0, 1, 2, 3, 4, 5, 6, or 7 bags

10. $18c \le 153$; $c \le 8.5$; 0, 1, 2, 3, 4, 5, 6, 7, or 8 CDs

Problem Solving

2. d; d; $21; $1.40

3. A   4. G

2-4 SOLVING TWO-STEP AND MULTI-STEP INEQUALITIES

Practice A

2. 3; 3; 3; 12; >; −4

3. 6; 6; 4; 5; 5; −1; 3; 3; $n > -\dfrac{1}{3}$

4. $x \ge -1$

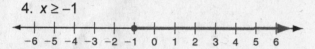

5. $z \le 2$

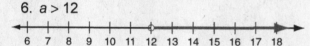

6. $a > 12$

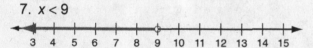

7. $x < 9$

8. $\dfrac{85 + 60 + x}{3} \ge 70$; $x \ge 65$; at least 65

Problem Solving

2. 0.15; 6200   3. C

4. H   5. A

2-5 SOLVING INEQUALITIES WITH VARIABLES ON BOTH SIDES

Practice A

2. −6y; 14; 6y; 6y; 14; 14; 14; 1

3. 15n; 18; 5n; 18; 18; 18; 5; 5; $n < -4\dfrac{2}{5}$

4. $x \le -2$

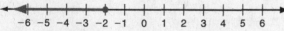

5. $b < 3$

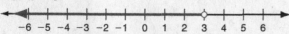

6. contradiction

7. identity

8. identity

9. $p - 0.15p + 12 < p$; $p > 80$; greater than $80

Problem Solving

2. 1,500y; 6,000; 6,000; 12

3. B   4. F

2-6 SOLVING COMPOUND INEQUALITIES

Practice A

1.

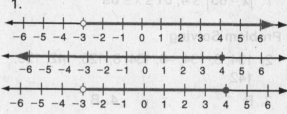

2.

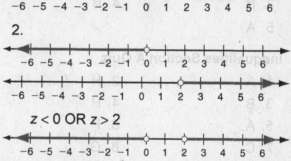

$z < 0$ OR $z > 2$

3. $x \le -1$ OR $x \ge 5$

4. $x > -4$ AND $x \le -1$

5. 5; 5; 5; 5; −3; 4

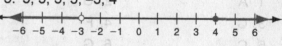

6. $400 \le m \le 600$

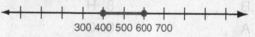

Problem Solving

2. 1; 5; or

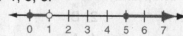

3. B   4. G

2-7 SOLVING ABSOLUTE-VALUE INEQUALITIES

Practice

2. –3; 3; 1; 1; 1; 1; –2; 4

4. $x \geq -4$ AND $x \leq 0$

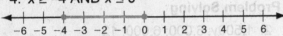

5. $x \geq -5$ AND $x \leq 5$

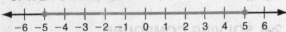

6. $x < -2$ OR $x > 2$

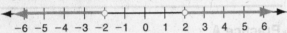

7. $|x - 85| \leq 4$; $81 \leq x \leq 89$

Problem Solving

2. 134; 8; 134; –8; 134; 8; 126; 142; 126; 142

3. B   4. B

5. A

Inequalities Section A Quiz

1. A   2. H
3. B   4. H
5. A   6. F
7. C   8. G
9. A   10. F

Inequalities Section B Quiz

1. A   2. G
3. C   4. F
5. C   6. G
7. B   8. H
9. A   10. G
11. C   12. C

Inequalities Chapter 2 Test

1. A   2. B
3. B   4. A
5. B   6. A
7. C   8. A
9. B   10. A
11. B   12. C

13. A   14. B
15. C   16. A
17. C   18. B
19. B   20. A
21. A

Holt McDougal Algebra 1

Answer Key Functions

3-1 GRAPHING RELATIONSHIPS

Practice A

2. staying the same   3. rising

4. Graph B   5. Graph C

6. Graph A

7. Possible answer: A subway train has up to 6 cars. Each car can hold 40 passengers.

Problem Solving

2.

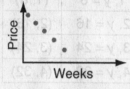

vertical; 200; discrete

3. B   4. H

5. A

3-2 RELATIONS AND FUNCTIONS

Practice A

1.

x	y
−2	5
−1	1
3	1
−1	−2

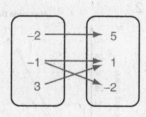

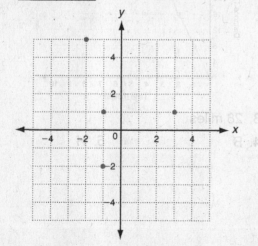

2.

x	y
5	3
4	3
3	3
2	3
1	3

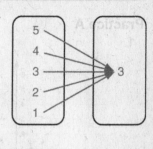

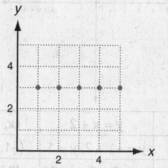

3. $\{0 \le x \le 4\}$; $\{0 \le y \le 4\}$; yes; Each domain value is paired with exactly one range value.

4. $\{8, 9\}$; $\{−3, −4, −6, −9\}$; no; Both domain values are paired with more than one range value.

Problem Solving

2. D: 12, 15, 18; R: 10.5, 11; y; yes

3. B .   4. H

3-3 WRITING FUNCTIONS

Practice A

2. $y = x − 3$ 3. $y = −3x$

4. independent; dependent

5. dependent; independent

6. 10; 2   7. −8; 2

8. −7; 20

9. $f(b) = 10b$; D: $\{0, 1, 2, 3, 4, 5, 6, 7\}$; R: $\{0, 10, 20, 30, 40, 50, 60, 70\}$

Problem Solving

2. $2x$; $30 − 2x$

3. B   4. F

5. C   6. G

Holt McDougal Algebra 1

3-4 GRAPHING FUNCTIONS

Practice A

1.

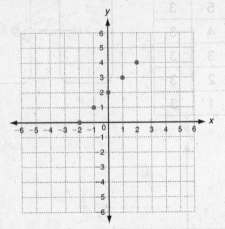

x	y = x + 2	(x, y)
−1	y = −1 + 2, y = 1	(−1, 1)
0	y = 0 + 2, y = 2	(0, 2)
1	y = 1 + 2, y = 3	(1, 3)
2	y = 2 + 2, y = 4	(2, 4)

2.

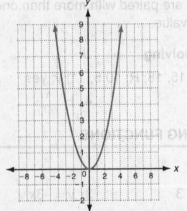

x	$y = x^2 + 2$	(x, y)
1	$y = 1 \div 2, y = \frac{1}{2}$	$\left(1, \frac{1}{2}\right)$
2	$y = 4 \div 2, y = 2$	(2, 2)
−1	$y = 1 \div 2, y = \frac{1}{2}$	$\left(-1, \frac{1}{2}\right)$
−2	$y = 4 \div 2, y = 2$	(−2, 2)

3.

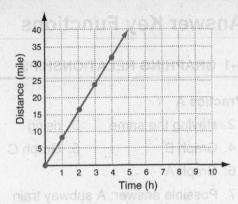

x	y = 8x	(x, y)
0	y = 8 • 0, y = 0	(0, 0)
1	y = 8 • 1, y = 8	(1, 8)
2	y = 8 • 2, y = 16	(2, 16)
3	y = 8 • 3, y = 24	(3, 24)
4	y = 8 • 4, y = 32	(4, 32)

about 28 miles

Problem Solving

1.

y = 8x	(x, y)
16	(2, 16)
24	(3, 24)
32	(4, 32)

2.

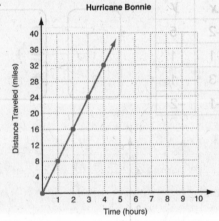

3. 28 miles

4. B   5. H

Holt McDougal Algebra 1

3-5 SCATTER PLOTS AND TREND LINES

Practice A

1.

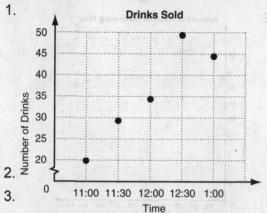

Drinks Sold

2.

3.

4. positive; as the temperature goes up, more people would go in the pool to cool off.

5. none; the height of a person has nothing to do with how many phone calls he or she makes

6. Possible answer: about 38 batteries

Problem Solving

1.

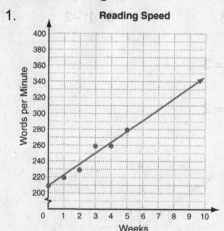

Reading Speed

2. positive correlation

3. about 320 wpm

4. C   5. H

6. B   7. F

3-6 ARITHMETIC SEQUENCES

Practice A

1. no   2. yes

3. 3   4. –6

5. $d = -10$; –20, –30, –40

---

6. $d = -2$; 92, 90, 88

7. 256   8. –19

9. 30   10. 20

11. $a_{12} = 30 + 11(20)$

Problem Solving

2. 0.15; 7; 1.05; 1.95

3. C   4. H

5. A   6. H

Functions Section A Quiz

1. C   2. G

3. C   4. H

5. B   6. F

7. C   8. F

Functions Section B Quiz

1. C   2. F

3. B   4. G

5. C   6. H

7. B   8. G

9. C

Functions Chapter 3 Test

1. B   2. C

3. A   4. A

5. B   6. C

7. A   8. C

9. A   10. B

11. C   12. B

13. C   14. B

15. A   16. B

Holt McDougal Algebra 1

Answer Key Linear Functions

4-1 IDENTIFYING LINEAR FUNCTIONS

Practice A

2. Each domain value (*x*-value) is paired with exactly one range value (*y*-value).

3. yes   4. yes

5. A constant change of +1 in *x* corresponds to a constant change of –2 in *y*.

6. $-x + y = -4$ 7. yes

8.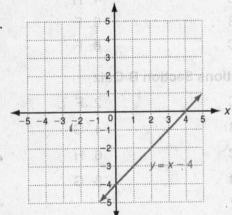

9.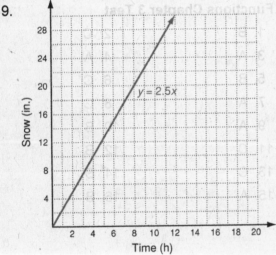

D: $x \geq 0$; R: $y \geq 0$

Problem Solving

2.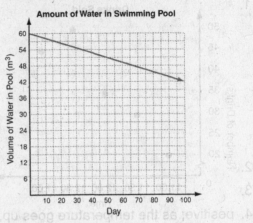

Amount of Water in Swimming Pool

D: $x \geq 0$; $0 \leq x \leq 333.3$
R: $0 \leq y \leq 60$

3. H   4. C

5. H

4-2 USING INTERCEPTS

Practice A

2. 4; –3   3. 1; –2

4.

   a. $x = 3$

   b. 3

   c. $y = 2$

   d. 2

   e.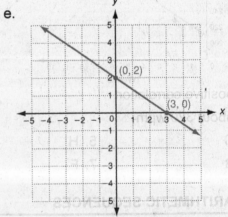

5.

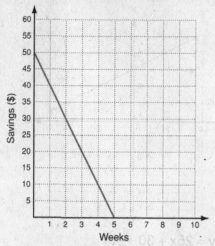

a. *x*-int: 5; *y*-int: 50

b. *x*-int: the amount of money after 5 weeks. *y*-int: the amount of money before she makes any withdrawals

Problem Solving

1.

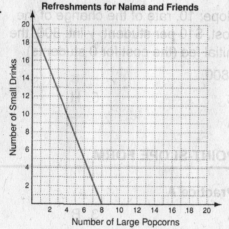

Refreshments for Naima and Friends

2. *y*-int: 400; *x*-int: 500

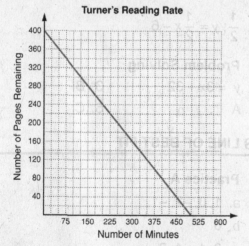

Turner's Reading Rate

3. B   **4.** H

5. C

Practice A

1. rise   2. run

3. rise; run

5. 2; 1; 2   6. $-3; 2; -\dfrac{3}{2}$

7. zero   8. negative

9. undefined

10. 35 mi/h; 12mi/h; 11mi/h; 39 mi/h; $\dfrac{1}{2}$ mi/h

Problem Solving

2. 9–11: 0.75; 11–12: 2;
   12–13: 3.5; 13–15: 2;
   12–13; 9–11; 11–12 and 13–15

3. 0; she was not moving during this time.

4. C   5. G

6. C

4-4 THE SLOPE FORMULA

Practice A

2. $3; -2; \dfrac{-4}{4}; -1$

3. $-2; 6; 0; 4; \dfrac{-8}{-4}; 2$

4. $-\dfrac{2}{3}$ 5. -2

6. 2; the profit increases $2 for every box sold.

7. $\dfrac{3}{2}$; For each additional crust made, 1.5 cups of flour are needed.

8. a. 0; 2*x*; 2; 2; –5   b. 0; 5*y*; 5; 5; –2

   c. $-5; -2; -2; -5; \dfrac{-2}{5}$

Problem Solving

2. –0.2; the number of pounds of flour used per day.

3. B   4. H

5. A

Holt McDougal Algebra 1

4-5 DIRECT VARIATION

Practice A

2.	$y = 4x - 10$	no	no	n/a
3.	$y = \frac{5}{2}x$	yes	yes	$\frac{5}{2}$

4.	$\frac{1}{5}; \frac{1}{5}; \frac{1}{5}$	yes	yes
5.	4; 2.5; 2	no	no

6. $\frac{1}{2}; \frac{1}{2}; 8; 4$ 7. $\frac{3}{2}; \frac{3}{2}; 15; \frac{45}{2}$

Problem Solving

2. yes; it can be written as $y = 4x$.

3. no; it cannot be written in the form $y = kx$.

4. 462 miles

5. A   6. H

7. C

4-6 SLOPE-INTERCEPT FORM

Practice A

2. –8

3. 3; –6; 6; 6; 11; –2; 11

4.

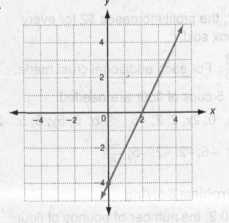

5. $y = -\frac{1}{2}x + 3$

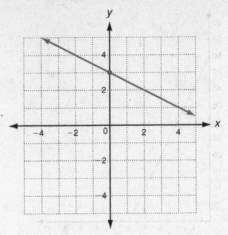

6. a. $y = 25x + 30$

b. slope: 25; number of desks per classroom; y-int: 30; number of spare desks

c. 630

Problem Solving

2. slope: 10, rate of the change of the cost, $10 per student; y-int: 300, the initial fee (the cost for 0 students)

3. $800

4. C   5. H

6. A

4-7 POINT-SLOPE FORM

Practice A

2. A   3. B

5. $y + 3 = -\frac{1}{2}(x - 5)$ 7. $y = -3x + 12$

9. $\frac{1}{2}; y = \frac{1}{2}x - 6$

Problem Solving

2. $y = 3x + 32$ 3. B

4. A   5. C

4-8 LINE OF BEST FIT

Practice A

1 a. 1, 0, –2, –1

b. 6

c. 0, 1, –1, 2

d. 6

Holt McDougal Algebra 1

e. neither

2 a. $y \approx 0.27x + 3.77$

   b. ≈ 0.997

   c. very well

   d. strong pos. correlation

3 a. $y = -0.13x + 4.28$

   b. ≈ -0.997

   c. very well

   d. strong neg. correlation

Problem Solving

1. a. $y = 0.8x + 2.3$

   b. Slope: for each hour practiced, a player will score 0.8 baskets; y-int.: a player who practices 0 h will score 2.3 baskets.

2. C

3. F

4. A

4-9 SLOPES OF PARALLEL AND PERPENDICULAR LINES

Practice A

2. $y - 5 = 6(x + 2)$; ⟨$y = -6x$⟩ ⟨$6x + y = 4$⟩ $y = 6$

3. $0; -2; 0; -2;$
The opposite sides have the same slope which means they are parallel. ABCD is a parallelogram because both pairs of opposite sides are parallel.

5. $y = 5x + 1$; ⟨$y = 3$⟩ $y = \frac{1}{5}x$; ⟨$x = 5$⟩

6. ⟨$y = \frac{1}{3}x - 2$⟩ $x = 2$; $y - 4 = 3(x + 3)$; ⟨$y = -3x + 9$⟩

7. $\frac{2}{5}; -\frac{5}{2}; -\frac{3}{7};$

   $\frac{2}{5}\left(-\frac{5}{2}\right) = -1$ so $\overline{AB}$ is perpendicular

to $\overline{BC}$. ABC is a right triangle because it contains a right angle.

Problem Solving

2. The slope of AB is $\frac{1}{4}$, the slope of AC is $-\frac{7}{4}$, and the slope of BC is $-\frac{1}{4}$. None of the slopes have a product of -1 so no sides are perpendicular.

3. C   4. C

4-10 TRANSFORMING LINEAR FUNCTIONS

Practice A

2. translation   3. reflection

4. translation 5 units up

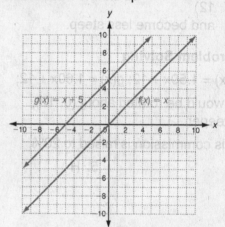

5. rotation (steeper) about $(0, -1)$

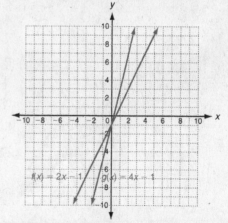

6. rotation (less steep) about $(0, 0)$ and translation 7 units down

       Holt McDougal Algebra 1

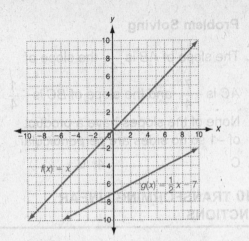

$f(x) = x$

$g(x) = \frac{1}{2}x - 7$

7. a. The graph will be translated 3 units up.

   b. The graph will be rotated about (0, 12)

   and become less steep.

Problem Solving

2. $f(x) = 1.50x + 12$; $g(x) = 1.60x + 12$;

   it would be rotated about (0, 12), steeper

3. His commission is raised to 20%.

4. B   5. H

6. A

Linear Functions Section A Quiz

1. B	2. A
3. B	4. C
5. C	6. A
7. C	8. B
9. B	10. C

Linear Functions Section B Quiz

1. A	2. C
3. B	4. B
5. B	6. C
7. A	8. C
9. A	10. C

Linear Functions Chapter 4 Test

1. B	2. A
3. C	4. B
5. B	6. A
7. B	8. A
9. A	10. B
11. A	12. C
13. A	14. C
15. C	

Holt McDougal Algebra 1

Answer Key Systems of Equations and Inequalities

5-1 SOLVING SYSTEMS BY GRAPHING

Practice A

2. –2; yes

    4; 4; 4; 8

    no; is not

3. (1, –2)

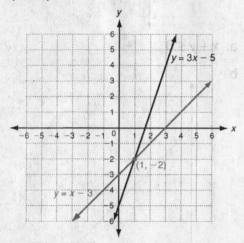

4. 20 miles; $80

Problem Solving

1. 20 months, $500

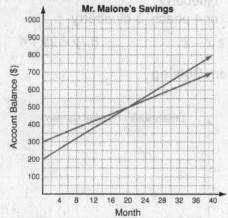

2. 7 months, 40 books

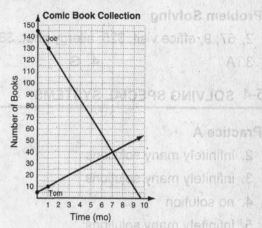

3. C   4. G

5. B

5-2 SOLVING SYSTEMS BY SUBSTITUTION

Practice A

1. 2x; 2; 2; x; 2; 2; 2; 2; 6; 2; 6

2. x – 3; x – 3; 4x; 4x; 4; 4; x; 7; 7; 7; 7; 4; 7; 4

3. (3, 12)   4. (2, 0)

5. a. $\begin{cases} y = 20x + 45 \\ y = 26x + 30 \end{cases}$

    b. 2.5

    c. $95

Problem Solving

2. 3 months; $155

3. B   4. H

5. A   6. H

5-3 SOLVING SYSTEMS BY ELIMINATION

Practice A

1. 2; 2; 2; 2; 12; 4; 2; 4

2. 2y; –7; 0y; –3; –3; –1; –1; 3; 3; 3; 9; 9; 9; –2; 2; 2; –1; 3; –1

3. 2; 4; –16; 5; 10; 5; 10; 5; 5; 2; 2; 2; 2; 2; –10; –2; –2; 5; 2; 5

Holt McDougal Algebra 1

4. (3, 4)   5. (6, −2)

6. (−8, −1)

Problem Solving

2. 57; 9; office visit, $25; allergy shot, $8

3. A   4. G

5-4 SOLVING SPECIAL SYSTEMS

Practice A

2. infinitely many solutions

3. infinitely many solutions

4. no solution

5. infinitely many solutions;
   consistent, dependent

6. no solution; inconsistent

7. They will always have the same amount
   of money.

   The graphs of these equations are the
   same line.

Problem Solving

2. 100 mi and $65

3. consistent and dependent;
   infinitely many solutions

4. A   5. H

6. B

5-5 SOLVING LINEAR INEQUALITIES

Practice A

2. yes   3. no

4. $y \leq 3 + x$

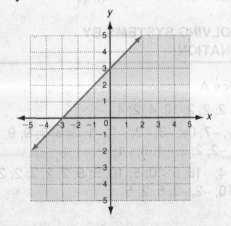

5. $y > -3x - 1$

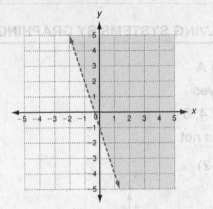

6. a. $x + y \leq 8$

b.

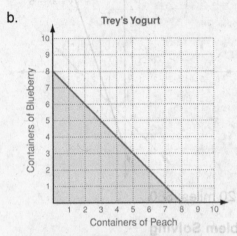

Trey's Yogurt

c. Possible answer: 2 peach, 6
   blueberry
   or 4 peach, 3 blueberry

7. $y \geq x - 2$ 8. $y < 2x + 4$

Problem Solving

2.

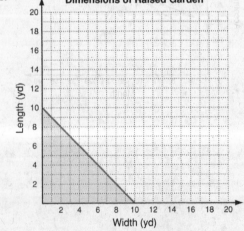

Dimensions of Raised Garden

3. A   4. G

5. B

Holt McDougal Algebra 1

5-6 SOLVING SYSTEMS OF LINEAR INEQUALITIES

Practice A

2. no

3. yes

4.

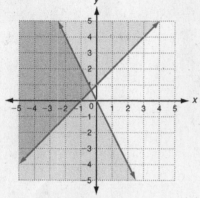

a. (–1, 0) and (–3, 2)

b. (0, –3) and (4, 0)

5.

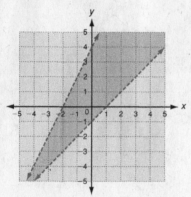

a. (0, 0) and (1, 2)

b. (1, 0) and (–4, 3)

6. a. $\begin{cases} x+y \geq 6 \\ 4x+2y \leq 20 \end{cases}$

b.

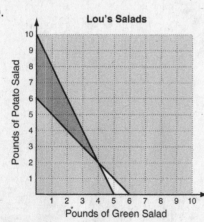

Lou's Salads

c. Any combination represented by the ordered pairs in the solution region.

d. 2 lb gr. salad, 5 lb potato salad; 3 lb gr. salad, 4 lb potato salad

Problem Solving

1.

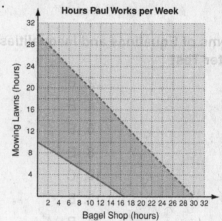

Hours Paul Works per Week

2. width of 1.25 ft, length of 7 ft; width of 1.4 ft, length of 7.5 ft

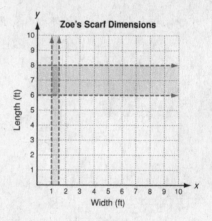

Zoe's Scarf Dimensions

3. A

4. H

Systems of Equations and Inequalities
Section A Quiz

1. C

2. G

3. B

4. H

5. C

6. F

7. B

8. G

9. A

10. H

Holt McDougal Algebra 1

Systems of Equations and Inequalities
Section B Quiz

1. C   2. G
3. A   4. H
5. B   6. H
7. C

Systems of Equations and Inequalities
Chapter Test

1. A   2. B
3. C   4. B
5. A   6. B
7. A   8. B
9. A   10. C
11. C   12. B
13. C   14. B

Holt McDougal Algebra 1

Answer Key Exponents and Polynomials

6-1 INTEGER EXPONENTS

Practice A

2. 2; 2; 2; 2; 16

3. −3; −3; −3; −3; −27

4. −1; −1; −1; −1; −1; −1; −1; −1

5. −1

6. $\dfrac{1}{64}$

7. 9

8. 2; 3; 1; 3; $\dfrac{1}{27}$

9. −2; $(-2)^4$; −2; −2; −2; −2; 16; $\dfrac{5}{16}$

10. $\dfrac{4}{x^3}$

11. $5b^2$

12. $\dfrac{1}{2k^4}$

13. $f^4 g$

14. $\dfrac{1}{4}$ gram or 0.25 gram

Problem Solving

2. $\dfrac{3}{8}$ and $\dfrac{3}{4}$ oz

3. $42\dfrac{2}{3}$ liters

4. B

5. H

6. C

6-2 RATIONAL EXPONENTS

Practice A

2. D

3. C

4. A

6. 3

7. 1

8. 12

9. 8

10. 9

11. 1

12. 32

13. x^8

14. 14 cm

Problem Solving

2. 9; 27; 51.3; 51.3 mi/h

3. C

4. G

5. A

6-3 POLYNOMIALS

Practice A

2. 3; 2

3. 5; 4

4. trinomial

5. monomial

6. binomial

7. $3x^2 - x + 12$; 3

8. $-g^5 + g^4 - 2g^3$; −1

9. $k^4 - k^3 + k^2 + 1$; 1

10. quadratic monomial 11. linear binomial

12. quartic trinomial 13. −3; 2; 13; −2; 5

14. 72 in^2

Problem Solving

2. 4; 360; −64; 360; 296 feet; 25; 900; −400; 900; 500 feet

3. $h = 0.25$: 0.9375 cubic feet; $h = 0.5$: 1 cubic foot

4. A

5. C

6-4 ADDING AND SUBTRACTING POLYNOMIALS

Practice A

2. $-20p^5 - 3p + 14$

3. $3m + 6$

4. $5y^2 + y + 12$

5. $6z^3 + 4z^2 + 5$

6. $12g^2 + 4g - 1$

7. $8k + 1$

8. $3s^3 + 5s + 20$

9. $9a^4 + 8a^2$

10. $9b^2 + b - 9$

11. $w + 8$

12. a. $2n + 2$

b. $8n + 20$

Problem Solving

2. $50x - 6$; 94 yards

3. B

4. C

6-5 MULTIPLYING POLYNOMIALS

Practice A

2. $15x^3$

3. $18y^5$

4. $15x + 21$

5. $8x^3 + 28x^2 + 12x$

6. $x^2 + 7x + 10$ 7. x^2; $-3x$; $4x$; -12;

                            $x^2 + x - 12$

8. x^3; $4x^2$; $7x$; $3x^2$; $12x$; 21;

   $x^3 + 7x^2 + 19x + 21$

9. a. w

   b. $w + 5$

   c. $w^2 + 5w$

   d. 24 in^2

   e. 36 in^2

Problem Solving

2. $(w + 4)$; w; $w^2 + 4w$;

   $22^2 + 4(22)$; 572 square feet

3. C   4. F

6-6 SPECIAL PRODUCTS OF BINOMIALS

Practice A

2. m; m; 3; 3; $m^2 + 6m + 9$

3. 2; 2; a; a; $4 + 4a + a^2$

4. $x^2 + 8x + 16$ 5. $a^2 + 14a + 49$

6. $64 + 16b + b^2$

8. y; y; 6; 6; $y^2 - 12y + 36$

9. 9; 9; x; x; $81 - 18x + x^2$

10. $y^2 - 14y + 49$ 11. $b^2 - 22b + 121$

12. $9 - 6x + x^2$

14. 4; y; $16 - y^2$ 15. x; 2; $x^2 - 4$

16. $x^2 - 64$ 17. $9 - y^2$

18. $x^2 - 1$

Problem Solving

2. $0.75x^2 - x - 65$; 2575 square feet

3. C   4. G

5. A

Exponents and Polynomials Section A Quiz

1. C   2. C

3. B   4. A

5. C   6. C

7. A   8. C

9. A   10. A

11. C   12. C

13. A   14. B

15. C   16. A

Exponents and Polynomials Section B Quiz

1. C   2. B

3. C   4. A

5. A   6. C

7. A   8. C

9. C   10. A

11. C   12. A

13. B   14. B

15. C

Exponents and Polynomials Chapter 6 Test

1. B   2. C

3. C   4. A

5. B   6. B

7. C   8. B

9. C   10. B

11. C   12. A

13. B   14. B

15. A   16. A

17. B   18. B

19. C   20. A

21. A   22. A

23. A   24. B

25. B   26. B

27. A   28. B

                            Holt McDougal Algebra 1

Answer Key Factoring Polynomials

7-1 FACTORS AND GREATEST COMMON FACTORS

Practice A

2. 40; 2; 10; 2; 5

3. 5; 5; 5; 5^3

5. 8

6. 12

7. 25

9. p

10. 6

11. $7y^2$

12. 16

13. 7

Problem Solving

2. 12 snacks of 4 carrot sticks and 3 apple slices

3. A

4. H

5. C

7-2 FACTORING BY GCF

Practice A

2. 5; m^3

3. 5; y^5; 2

4. $2y^2(5 + 6y)$

5. $6t(-2t^4 + 1)$

6. $3x^2(2x^2 + 5x + 1)$

7. $5t(-t + 8)$

8. $(d + 2)(4d + 9)$

9. $(x - 5)(12 + 7x)$

10. $3n^2$; 12; 3; 3; $(n + 3)(n^2 + 4)$

11. $(2x + 5)(x^2 + 1)$

12. $2y^3$; 6; y; 2; y; y; y; 2; $(y - 2)(2y^2 - 3)$

13. $(m - 3)(4m^2 - 5)$

Problem Solving

2. $-3(x^2 + 9x - 275)$

3. C

4. H

5. B

7-3 FACTORING $x^2 + bx + c$

Practice A

2. 4; 1

3. 5; 4

4. $(x + 7)(x + 3)$

5. $(x + 6)(x + 5)$

6. $(x + 8)(x + 2)$

7. 6; 2

8. 5; 3

9. 16; 1

10. $(x - 9)(x - 3)$

11. $(x - 4)(x - 11)$

12. $(x - 8)(x - 5)$

13. 10; 4

14. 3; 1

15. 8; 4

16. 12; 2

17. 14; 2

18. 5; 2

19. $(x + 3)(x - 5)$

20. $(x + 2)(x - 10)$

21. $(x + 6)(x - 8)$

Problem Solving

2. a. $x + 5$; $x + 5$

   b. 12 in. by 19 in.

3. C

4. H

5. B

7-4 FACTORING $ax^2 + bx + c$

Practice A

2. 2; 3; 2; 5

3. $(3x + 5)(x + 4)$

4. $(3x + 2)(2x + 5)$

5. $(2x + 1)(4x + 7)$

6. $(2x + 3)(4x + 1)$

7. 1; 1; 8

8. 3; 7; 3; 2

9. $(3x - 5)(2x - 5)$

10. $(5x - 2)(x - 4)$

11. $(7x - 5)(3x - 1)$

12. $(4x - 3)(3x - 4)$

14. 3; 4; 1; 1

15. $(x + 2)(5x - 3)$

16. $(4x + 3)(x - 3)$

17. $(2x + 1)(2x - 7)$

18. $(3x + 4)(2x - 5)$

20. 2; 1; 3; 4

21. $-1(5x + 2)(4x - 3)$

Problem Solving

2. 4; 1; 0 ft

3. C

4. F

5. B

7-5 FACTORING SPECIAL PRODUCTS

Practice A

2. 1; $3x$; $3x$; 1; $3x$; 2; 1

3. $(x - 9)^2$

4. $(6x + 2)^2$

6. 6 is not a perfect square.

7. a. $x + 4$ in.

   b. $4(x + 4)$ in.

8. 3; 3

9. $2p$; 7; $2p$; 7

Holt McDougal Algebra 1

10. $(t^3 + 12)(t^3 - 12)$ 11. $(4x^5 + y)(4x^5 - y)$

12. 20 is not a perfect square.

Problem Solving

2. $12x - 60$; 240 cm

3. C   4. F

7-6 CHOOSING A FACTORING METHOD

Practice A

2. yes

3. yes   4. yes

5. no; $2(m + 9)(m + 1)$

6. no; $2(p - 4)(p + 3)$

8. $3w(w + 5)^2$ 9. $12y(x - 2)^2$

10. $-3d(d - 10)(d + 10)$ 11. $2(a + 4)(a - 4)$

12. $5(m + 3)(m - 4)$ 14. $2(x + 3)(x + 1)$

15. $(f^2 + 4)(f - 3)$ 16. $-3(k - 6)(2k - 1)$

Problem Solving

2. $4\pi(2k - 1)^2$; $4\pi m^2$

3. C   4. G

5. C   6. H

Factoring Polynomials Section A Quiz

1. A   2. H

3. B   4. G

5. C   6. H

7. B   8. H

9. C   10. H

11. B   12. G

13. B   14. F

15. B   16. G

Factoring Polynomials Section B Quiz

1. A   2. H

3. B   4. F

5. A   6. H

7. C   8. G

9. C   10. F

11. C   12. F

13. C   14. H

Factoring Polynomials Chapter 7 Test

1. A   2. C

3. A   4. A

5. C   6. A

7. A   8. B

9. B   10. C

11. B   12. B

13. B   14. B

15. A   16. A

17. C   18. B

19. B   20. C

21. A   22. B

23. B

Holt McDougal Algebra 1

Answer Key Quadratic Functions and Equations

8-1 IDENTIFYING QUADRATIC FUNCTIONS

Practice A

2. yes; It can be written in the form $y = ax^2 + bx + c$.

3.

x	$y = x^2 - 4$	(x, y)
–2	$y = (-2)^2 - 4 = 0$	(–2, 0)
–1	$y = (-1)^2 - 4 = -3$	(–1, –3)
0	$y = (0)^2 - 4 = -4$	(0, –4)
1	$y = (1)^2 - 4 = -3$	(1, –3)
2	$y = (2)^2 - 4 = 0$	(2, 0)

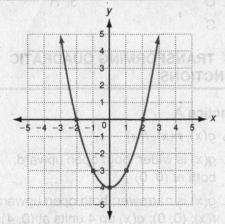

4. downward   5. upward

6. (–2, –6)   7. minimum: –6

8. D: all real numbers; R: $y \geq -6$

Problem Solving

1.

t	0	1	2	3	4
$f(t)$	4	52	68	52	4

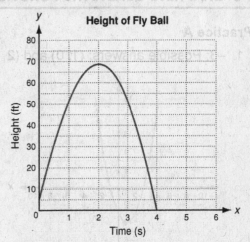

Height of Fly Ball

2. No; the second differences are not constant.

3. B   4. H

8-2 CHARACTERISTICS OF QUADRATIC FUNCTIONS

Practice A

2. –2   3. no zeros

5. $x = -4$ 6. $x = 5$

8. 1; –10; 5; $x = 5$; (5, 15)

9. 2; –8; 2; $x = 2$; (2, –11)

Problem Solving

2. (50, 30)   3. B

4. H   5. C

6. G   7. C

Holt McDougal Algebra 1

8-3 GRAPHING QUADRATIC FUNCTIONS

Practice A

1. −3; Possible answers: (1, 0) and (2, 5)

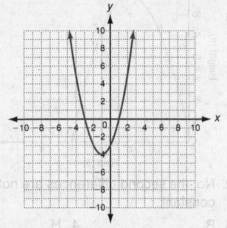

2. $x = -2$; (−2, 18); 10; Possible answers: (−1, 16) and (1, 0)

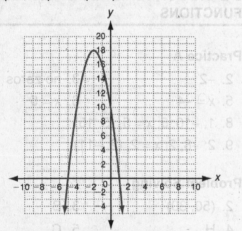

3. 16 feet; 1 second; 2 seconds

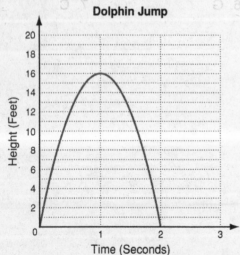

Dolphin Jump

Problem Solving

1.

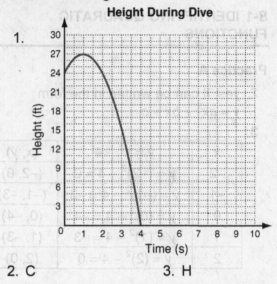

Height During Dive

2. C   3. H

4. C

8-4 TRANSFORMING QUADRATIC FUNCTIONS

Practice A

2. $g(x)$, $h(x)$, $f(x)$

4. $g(x)$ is wider; both open upward; both at (0, 0)

5. $g(x)$ is narrower; both open upward; $f(x)$: (0, 0); $g(x)$ up 4 units at (0, 4)

6. same; $f(x)$ opens upward, $g(x)$ opens downward; $f(x)$: (0, 0); $g(x)$ down 1 unit at (0, −1)

7. a. 400; 256

   b. vertical; 144

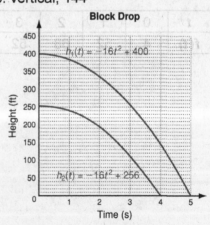

Block Drop

$h_1(t) = -16t^2 + 400$

$h_2(t) = -16t^2 + 256$

c. ball dropped from 400 ft: 5 s; ball
   dropped from 256 ft: 4 s

Problem Solving

2.

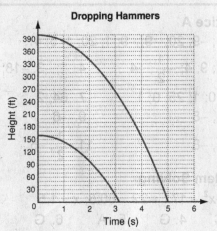

Dropping Hammers

3. 5 seconds; 3.2 seconds

4. F   5. C

8-5 SOLVING QUADRATIC EQUATIONS BY GRAPHING

Practice A

2.

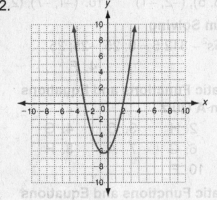

$x = -3$ or $x = 2$

3.

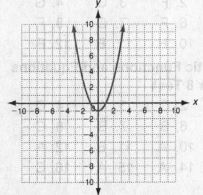

4.

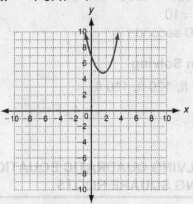

no real solution

5. 3 seconds

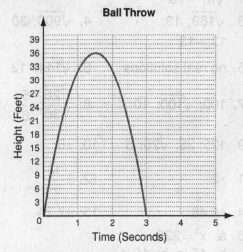

Ball Throw

Problem Solving

2. 8 seconds; 400 feet   3. $x = 3$; $x = 13$

4. C   5. G

6. C

8-6 SOLVING QUADRATIC EQUATIONS BY FACTORING

Practice A

1. $a = 0$; $b = 0$ 3. 5; 1

4. $x = -2$; $x = -6$ 5. $x = \dfrac{4}{3}$; $x = 3$

7. $x + 1$; $x + 1$; -1

8. 9; 3; $x - 9$; $x + 3$; 9; -3

9. $x + 3$; $x + 5$; $x + 3$; $x + 5$; -3; -5

10. $x = 5$; $x = 1$ 11. $x = 6$; $x = -2$

Holt McDougal Algebra 1

12. a. $-16t^2 + 1600 = 0$
    b. $t = 10$
    c. 10 seconds

Problem Solving

2. 200 ft, 120 ft, 160 ft

3. B   4. F

5. B

8-7 SOLVING QUADRATIC EQUATIONS BY USING SQUARE ROOTS

Practice A

1. $\sqrt{a}$; $-\sqrt{a}$

3. $\sqrt{169}$; 13;   4. $\sqrt{900}$; 30
   13; -13

5. no real solutions   6. $\sqrt{144}$; 12

7. 100; $\sqrt{100}$; 10   8. $\sqrt{\dfrac{25}{36}}$; $\dfrac{5}{6}$

9. 125; 25; $\sqrt{25}$; 5   10. ± 6

11. ± 2 12. $\pm\dfrac{1}{5}$

14. ± 5.48 15. ± 2.24

16. a. $x^2 = 225$
    b. 15 in. by 15 in.

Problem Solving

2. 20 inches   3. 11.5 inches

4. B   5. G

6. B

8-8 COMPLETING THE SQUARE

Practice A

2. 36   3. 16

5. 9; 1, 5   6. 1; -4, 6

7. 25; -2, -8

8. $x^2 - 4x = 5$; 4; 5, -1

9. $x^2 - 4x - 12 = 0$; 4; -2, 6

10. a. width $= w$; length $= w + 6$
    b. $w^2 + 6w = 91$
    c. 9
    d. $w = 7$, $l = 13$

Problem Solving

2. 2.5 ft   3. C   4. G   5. B

8-9 THE QUADRATIC FORMULA AND THE DISCRIMINANT

Practice A

2. 1; -9; 20; -9; -9; 1; 20; 1; 5, 4

3. 2; 9; 4; $-\dfrac{1}{2}$, -4 4. 1; -3; -18; 6, -3

6. 10; 1; 25; 0; 1   7. 64; 2

8. 8, -8 9. -6

10. 4, -8 11. $\dfrac{1}{2}$, -5

Problem Solving

2. $8x^2 + 17x + 22 = 80.5$; $x = 1.5$

3. C   4. G   5. A   6. G

8-10 NONLINEAR SYSTEMS

Practice A

1. (2, 2), (3, 7)   2. (1, 3), (2, 2)

4. no solution   5. $(-1, -2)$, (2, 7)

6. $(-5, 0)$, (6, 11)   8. $(-2, -1)$, $(-1, 0)$

9. $(-3, 5)$, $(-2, -1)$ 10. $(-1, -7)$, (2, -1)

Problem Solving

2. $0.5s^2 - 312.5 = 0$; 25, -25; 25

3. A   4. F

Quadratic Functions and Equations Section A Quiz

1. B   2. H   3. C   4. G

5. A   6. G   7. A   8. H

9. B   10. F

Quadratic Functions and Equations Section B Quiz

1. B   2. F   3. C   4. G

5. C   6. F   7. C   8. F

9. A   10. H   11. B   12. F

Quadratic Functions and Equations Chapter 8 Test

1. B   2. C   3. A   4. C

5. B   6. B   7. B   8. C

9. A   10. A   11. B   12. A

13. C   14. A   15. A   16. C

    Holt McDougal Algebra 1

Answer Key Exponential Functions

9-1 GEOMETRIC SEQUENCES

Practice A

2. 10; 100,000, 1,000,000, 10,000,000

3. $\frac{1}{2}$; 8, 4, 2

4. −5; 2500, −12,500, 62,500

5. 2048   6. −384

7. 1792   8. 3; 9; 729

9. −2; −2; −8192

Problem Solving

2. 19,683 branches; 98,415 branches

3. B   4. H

5. A

9-2 EXPONENTIAL FUNCTIONS

Practice A

1. 10.6 feet

3. no, as the x-values increase by 1, the y-values are not multiplied by a constant.

4.

y	(x, y)
2	(0, 2)
6	(1, 6)
18	(2, 18)

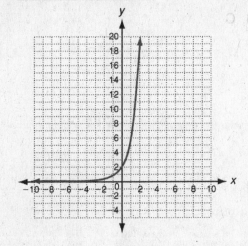

5.

$y = -2(4)^x$	y	(x, y)
$y = -2(4)^{-2}$	−0.125	(−2, −0.125)
$y = -2(4)^{-1}$	−0.5	(−1, −0.5)
$y = -2(4)^{0}$	−2	(0, −2)
$y = -2(4)^{1}$	−8	(1, −8)
$y = -2(4)^{2}$	−32	(2, −32)

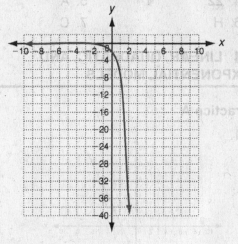

Problem Solving

1. b.

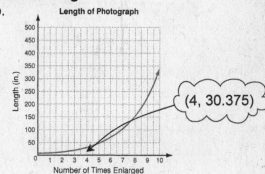

Length of Photograph

(4, 30.375)

2. 4 years; 32 years   3. 2210

4. B   5. J

9-3 EXPONENTIAL GROWTH AND DECAY

Practice A

2. 2200; 0.02; 6; 2478

3. $200(1 + 0.08)^{12}$; $503.63

4. $25,335.40

5. 35,000; 0.06; 12; 12; 10
$63,678.89

Holt McDougal Algebra 1

6. $35,000\left(1+\dfrac{0.08}{4}\right)^{20}$;

$52,008.16

8. 2300; 0.04; 10; 1529

Problem Solving

2. $y = 500\left(1+\dfrac{0.02}{12}\right)^{12t}$; $541.61

3. $y = 4500(0.985)^t$; 3084

4. 22   5. A

6. H   7. C

9-4 LINEAR, QUADRATIC, AND EXPONENTIAL MODELS

Practice A

1.

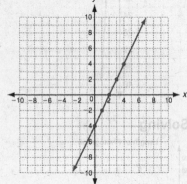

2.

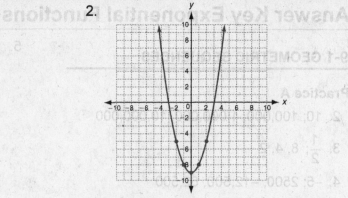

quadratic

4. linear

5. quadratic

6. a. linear

   b. $y = 0.45x$

   c. $3.60

Problem Solving

1.

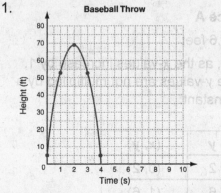

2. $y = 1.29x$ 3. $y = 14(2)^x$; 896

4. A   5. G

6. C

Holt McDougal Algebra 1

Practice A

1.

$y = 5x + 10$	
x	y
0	10
1	15
2	20
3	25
4	30

5

$y = 1 + 5^x$	
x	y
0	2
1	6
2	26
3	126
4	626

156

2.

$y = 3x^2 + 3x$	
x	y
0	0
1	6
2	18
3	36
4	60

15

0

60

$y = 3 + 3^x$	
x	y
0	4
1	6
2	12
3	30
4	84

20

4

84

$y = 5x^2 + 5x$	
x	y
0	0
1	10
2	30
3	60
4	100

25

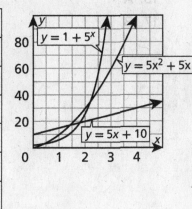

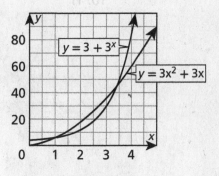

a. The linear function has the least rate of change and the exponential function has the greatest rate of change.

b. The function with the greatest rate of change has the greatest difference between the y-values at $x = 0$ and $x = 4$.

Holt McDougal Algebra 1

Problem Solving

1. Slope: Both are saving at the same rate, $50 per month. y-intercept: The y-intercept for George's account is $125. The y-intercept for Julie's account is $200. Julie started with more money than George.

2. B

3. F

Exponential Functions Section A Quiz

1. B   2. G

3. B   4. H

5. A   6. G

7. B   8. G

9. A   10. H

Exponential Functions Section B Quiz

1. C   2. G

3. B   4. H

5. C   6. H

7. C   8. H

9. A   10. F

11. A

Exponential Functions Chapter 9 Test

1. B   2. A

3. A   4. B

5. B   6. A

7. B   8. B

9. B   10. C

11. A   12. A

13. C   14. B

15. A   16. B

17. B

Answer Key Data Analysis and Probability

10-1 ORGANIZING AND DISPLAYING DATA

Practice A

2. 32 years   3. Hound Shark

4. March   5. 4

6. $0.50

7.

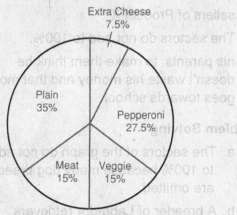

Pizza Orders

Extra Cheese 7.5%

Plain 35%

Pepperoni 27.5%

Meat 15%

Veggie 15%

It compares each type of pizza to the total number of pizzas.

Problem Solving

1.

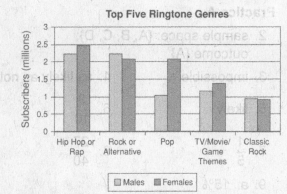

Top Five Ringtone Genres

☐ Males ■ Females

2. For Pop, the bar for females is twice as tall as the bar for males.

3. C   4. F

5. C

10-2 FREQUENCY AND HISTOGRAMS

Practice A

1.

stem	Miles Driven leaves
3	2
4	3 8
5	2 4 4 7
6	5 8
7	2 3 4 8
8	3
9	6 8

Key: 4|3 means 43

2. b. 5

   c. 53

   d. Period 5; 1

3.

Frequency
6
4
4
3
4

4.

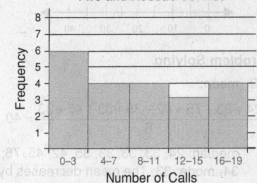

Fire and Rescue Service

5. 4–7, 8–11, 16–19

    Holt McDougal Algebra 1

Problem Solving

2.

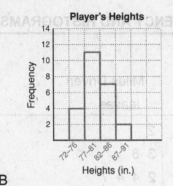

Player's Heights

3. B

10-3 DATA DISTRIBUTIONS

Practice

2. 2, 3, 3, 5, 5, 5, 5
   mean: 4   median: 5
   mode: 5   range: 3

3. mean: 11   median: 10.5
   mode: 8 and 12   range: 9

5. outlier: 11, decreases mean by 8.5,
   median by 2.5, no effect on mode,
   increases range by 28

6a. mean, 44

6b. median, 50, because it is higher than
    the mean.

7a. 8, 10, 14, 15, 18, 22, 22, 30, 33

7b. 8, 12, 18, 26, 33

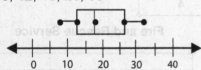

Problem Solving

2. mean:

$$\frac{24 + 33 + 76 + 42 + 35 + 33 + 45 + 33}{8} = 40.125,$$

   median: 24, 33, 33, 33, 35, 42, 45, 76;
   34, mode: 33; The mean decreases by
   5.125, median decreases by 1.

3. B   4. F

5. B

10-4 MISLEADING GRAPHS AND STATISTICS

Practice A

2. Lazaro scored more than twice as
   much as the other players.

3. The vertical axis does not start at 0 and
   the categories on the horizontal axis
   are not at equal time intervals.

4. that the cost of Product X decreased
   very rapidly

5. sellers of Product X

6. The sectors do not add to 100%.

7. his parents; to make them think he
   doesn't waste his money and that most
   goes towards school.

Problem Solving

2. a. The sectors of the graph do not add
      to 100% because many dog breeds
      are omitted.

   b. A breeder of Labrador retrievers
      might use the graph to
      overemphasize the popularity of the
      breed.

3. C   4. F

10-5 EXPERIMENTAL PROBABILITY

Practice A

2. sample space: {A, B, C, D};
   outcome {A}

3. impossible   4. as likely as not

5. likely   6. $\frac{3}{10}$

7. $\frac{1}{5}$ 8. $\frac{27}{40}$

9. a. 15%

   b. 45

Problem Solving

1. b. as likely as not

2. a. 0.267 or 26.7%

   b. 152 hits

3. A   4. H

Holt McDougal Algebra 1

10-6 THEORETICAL PROBABILITY

Practice A

2. 30%

3. $16\frac{2}{3}$%

4. 25%

5. 90%

6. $\frac{1}{4}$

7. 0.5

8. 95%

9. a. 5

   b. 1

   c. $\frac{1}{5}$

10. a. 9

    b. 7

    c. $\frac{7}{9}$

11. a. $\frac{2}{5}$

    b. $\frac{11}{15}$

    c. 1:2

Problem Solving

2. $\frac{3}{4}$

3. 144 tiles

4. B

5. H

6. A

10-7 INDEPENDENT AND DEPENDENT EVENTS

Practice A

2. dependent; a marble selected and not replaced reduces the number to choose from.

3. a. independent

   b. $\frac{1}{36}$

4. a. dependent

   b. $\frac{1}{19}$

5. a. independent; $\frac{7}{100} = 7\%$

   b. dependent; $\frac{1}{45} \approx 2.2\%$

   c. dependent; $\frac{7}{45} \approx 15.6\%$

6. $\frac{28}{45} \approx 62.2\%$

7. $\frac{1}{45} \approx 2.2\%$

Problem Solving

2. $\frac{2}{15}$

3. $\frac{30}{90} = \frac{1}{3}$

4. $\frac{4}{15}$

5. $\frac{4}{15}$

6. C

7. F

Data Analysis and Probability Section A Quiz

1. B

2. H

3. B

4. H

5. C

6. H

7. A

8. H

9. C

10. H

Data Analysis and Probability Section B Quiz

1. C

2. F

3. C

4. G

5. A

6. H

7. B

8. H

9. C

10. H

11. C

Data Analysis and Probability Chapter 10 Test

1. A

2. A

3. B

4. B

5. C

6. B

7. C

8. B

9. C

10. C

11. A

12. A

13. A

14. B

15. B

Holt McDougal Algebra 1

Answer Key End of Course Assessment

END OF COURSE ASSESSMENT

1. C	2. H
3. A	4. G
5. C	6. F
7. B	8. G
9. C	10. G
11. C	12. H
13. A	14. H
15. C	16. F
17. A	18. F
19. B	20. G
21. B	22. H
23. C	24. G
25. B	26. H
27. B	28. G
29. C	30. H
31. A	32. H
33. C	34. H
35. C	36. F
37. B	38. F
39. C	40. H
41. C	42. H
43. B	

Holt McDougal Algebra 1